"Why you...!"

Natalie's hand raced through the air, but before it could land a stinging slap on Flynn's cheek, he caught her wrist.

"I think I warned you not to do that, Natalie. You might not enjoy the consequences, although I would!" His gaze dropped to her mouth and stayed there in a look she could feel in every cell of her body, before abruptly he tossed her hand away. "Let's go. We've wasted enough time."

Jennifer Taylor was born in Liverpool, England, and still lives in the northwest, several miles outside of the city. Books have always been a passion of hers, so it seemed natural to choose a library career—a wise decision as the library was where she met her husband, Bill. Twenty years and two children later they are still happily married and she is still working in the library, with the added bonus that she has discovered how challenging and enjoyable writing romantic fiction can be!

Books by Jennifer Taylor

HARLEQUIN ROMANCE
3142—LOVESPELL

HARLEQUIN PRESENTS
1326—A MAGICAL TOUCH
1349—TENDER PURSUIT

Desert Moon
Jennifer Taylor

Harlequin Books

TORONTO • NEW YORK • LONDON
AMSTERDAM • PARIS • SYDNEY • HAMBURG
STOCKHOLM • ATHENS • TOKYO • MILAN
MADRID • WARSAW • BUDAPEST • AUCKLAND

ISBN 0-373-17270-2

DESERT MOON

First North American Publication 1996.

Copyright © 1995 by Jennifer Taylor.

CHAPTER ONE

WHAT a day!

Flynn O'Rourke poured himself a generous measure of Scotch then loosened his tie as he walked over to the sofa and slumped down on the cushions. He took a deep swallow of the liquor and closed his eyes while he let it trickle down his throat and burn away the edges of his frustration.

It was hard to believe that so much could go wrong. He'd been on his way to the airport in Rome when the call had come through. He'd turned right around and gone back then spent the next few hours sorting out the mess before he could even think of leaving again. But the vacation he'd promised himself was out of the question now. Some might see what had happened as a run of bad luck, but Flynn didn't believe in luck, either good or bad. There was someone behind it all. He had his suspicions but that was all they were as yet. What he needed was the evidence to back them up, and while part of him shied away from what he might uncover it had to be done.

Flynn raised his glass again, rolling twelve-year-old Scotch over his palate while he savoured its smoothness as he looked round the immaculate room. The flat wasn't his taste, too regimented and orderly, but he couldn't fault Marcus Cole's choice of whisky. It had been a gamble coming here but Marcus had readily offered him the use of his flat while he was away when Flynn had turned up on his doorstep after flying back from Rome.

He'd accepted without question what Flynn had told him about his own place being uninhabitable, thanks to a neighbour who'd gone away and left the bath running. Now Flynn intended to make the most of the opportunity.

He raised his glass again then realised it was almost empty. He got up and poured another couple of fingers of best malt into the heavy cut-crystal and sipped it more slowly. Whisky like this deserved to be savoured and accorded due respect, not bolted back like cheap bar-room bourbon. The trouble was he'd been living out of a suitcase for so long now that he'd almost forgotten what it was like to enjoy a few home comforts, a touch of refinement. His own small service flat was purely basic, a place to sleep when he was in England, which wasn't very often. Staying here could serve a dual purpose, give him chance to reacquaint himself with life how it should be lived. Try hard enough, and enlist the help of a drop of good malt, and it was possible to find a silver lining to any dark cloud!

Cradling the glass in one hand, Flynn walked to the state-of-the-art music system housed in one of the ceiling-high black ash units which ran the length of the large room. He rolled a drop more Scotch over his tongue as he riffled through the neat stack of CDs, smiling sardonically as he found Black Sabbath cheek by jowl with Brahms. Who would have thought that Marcus was into heavy metal? It didn't seem to fit the sophisticated criminal lawyer image, but there again, how much did one ever really know about people you did business with?

He set the glass down as he switched on the player then slid the silvery disc into its slot, but before he could press the button to start it playing the telephone rang. Impatiently, Flynn glanced across the room before he

heard the answering machine cut in to take the call.
Touching a finger to the play button, he went back to
the sofa and stretched out as the first few chords of
'Paranoid' hit the air.

'Marcus, it's me, Natalie. Oh, I wish you were home.
I hate talking to this machine but I'm absolutely desperate! You just have to help me!'

The woman paused as though marshalling her
thoughts and Flynn eased himself up against the back
of the sofa, both the drink and the throbbing beat of
the music forgotten as his attention centred on the sweetly
husky tones once more issuing from the machine.

'Remember me telling you about that account I was
chasing, the *really* big one? Well, I think I've got it. The
trouble is Damian Renshaw, who owns the company. He
appears to be finding it difficult to understand that my
only role is to ensure that the advertising campaign runs
smoothly!' There was a trace of exasperation in the
woman's voice now. 'He seems to think that I should be
offering a more *personal* service to him at least, and while
I want the contract there are limits beyond which I am
not prepared to go. And Damian Renshaw isn't within
a million miles of them!

'But that, hopefully, is where you come in, Marcus.
Damian is taking a party to the opera tonight and has
invited me along. I should go just to keep him sweet but
I want to make it clear that the only relationship I'm
interested in with him is a business one. I...' The woman,
Natalie, paused, then rushed on so fast that Flynn
frowned as he tried to follow the flow of words. 'I told
Damian that I would be bringing a friend along, a very
dear friend, and left him to make up his own mind what
that meant! So please, please, Marcus, you have to come!
I know it's a huge imposition to ask you like this at the

very last moment but I'm desperate and I know you won't let me down.

'If you could come along and just do your best to convince Damian he's wasting his time then I shall be eternally grateful. This account is worth a fortune and it could make a huge difference to my career, so...' The woman ran through all the details as to where Marcus should meet her then said goodbye and hung up.

Flynn swirled the half-forgotten whisky round the glass, a faint smile playing around his mouth as he wondered if the unknown Natalie was as gorgeous as that sexy, smoky voice of hers.

He set the glass down on a side-table, ignoring the black coaster placed there precisely for such an event, and got up to walk over to the phone and press the replay button so that he could listen to the message again, savouring, in much the same way as he had savoured that first mouthful of Scotch, the seductive softness of Natalie's tones before a few salient points struck him sharply.

The woman had left no call-back number where Marcus could reach her, probably because he knew it and because she was confident that he would do as she asked. Add that to what she had said and it left Flynn in little doubt that Natalie knew Marcus extremely well. Interesting!

Walking back to the sofa, Flynn sank down again and closed his eyes, letting the music throb and pound his senses, yet it couldn't quite dispel the idea which was forming at the back of his mind...

Where was he?

Natalie Walters pushed back the sleeve of her black moiré silk cocktail suit and shot another anxious look at the large-faced, strictly utilitarian watch strapped to her slender wrist. There were less than ten minutes left before the start of the first act and even now people were drifting inside to take their seats. Where on earth was Marcus?

The glass doors opened to admit another late-comer but it took only a split-second for her eyes to sweep over the man who'd just come in before she dismissed him, although she must have been one of the few women in the foyer who did so. Tall, lean and blond, and almost sinfully handsome, he drew the eyes of every red-blooded woman the right side of sixty, plus the eyes of those who'd passed that mark several years before! Natalie had no trouble in turning her gaze away, however, for the simple reason that the man wasn't Marcus.

'Seems your friend is a trifle late, Natalie, darling. Are you sure he is coming?'

Natalie fixed a smile to lips which wanted to clamp together in a mean line, curbing the faint feeling of revulsion she always experienced around Damian Renshaw. It wasn't something she could explain because there was nothing about his appearance to warrant it. Touching forty, smoothly urbane, just a shade too corpulent thanks to good living and a dislike of exercise, Damian was considered one of the world's most eligible bachelors. He had inherited the huge Renshaw cosmetic house from his father five years ago and since then rarely been seen without a beautiful woman hanging on his arm. Natalie, however, failed to share their interest in him. Bidding for this contract to promote the new Renshaw perfume would have been a whole lot simpler if Damian hadn't decided that she should be part of the package. She'd tried to explain to her boss back at the agency what the problem was but he had been unsympathetic. In these days of recession contracts were hard to come by, especially lucrative ones like this. Natalie would just have to sort it out by herself while not antagonising Renshaw.

'Penny for them, sweetness.' Damian touched her hand, bending closer to smile at her. 'You aren't worried that your friend might not come, are you?' He stroked his fingers over the back of her hand again, his smile increasing in meaning as he stared straight into her eyes. 'Don't be. I shall be only too pleased to escort you tonight, Natalie.'

Surreptitiously, Natalie drew her hand away, resisting the urge to rub it against her skirt to erase the feel of Damian's slightly moist fingers from her skin. 'That's very kind of you, Damian, but I'm sure there won't be any need. Perhaps he has been held up *en route*. You know what the traffic can be like.'

'Of course. But my offer still stands, Natalie...'

'Natalie! Sorry I'm so late, honey. Were you starting to worry I wouldn't make it?' There was a deep laugh then Natalie found herself being swung round and clamped against a hard body while unmistakably male lips captured hers in a kiss which could only be classed as expert!

For a moment she stood immobile, stunned by what had happened and, if she was honest, by the feel of the man's mouth on hers, then suddenly came to her senses. She pushed against the man's chest, feeling the hardness of muscle under the smooth white silk shirt, the rigidity of flesh honed to perfection, as she glared up into a pair of laughing sea-green eyes.

'I really don't——'

'Don't think this is the time or the place for me to kiss you?' The man laughed again, the sound rumbling deeply in his chest so that she could feel the tremors it

aroused in her fingertips. Instinctively she curled her
fingers into her palms and pushed him harder, succeeding in making a few inches of space between their
bodies this time.

'Look, I have no idea what you think you are——'

The stranger pressed a long finger to her lips, effectively cutting off the heated flow of words as he looked
over her head to wink conspiratorially at Damian, who
was standing stiffly watching the exchange. 'Has quite
a temper when she gets going. It's one of the things I
love most about her. You must be Damian Renshaw, of
course. I'm delighted to meet you. Natalie has told me
about you and this contract she's been working on.'

The man set Natalie slightly away from him as he held
his hand out to Damian, although he didn't let her go
completely. Natalie drew a shuddery disbelieving breath.
This couldn't be happening! She couldn't be standing
here in the middle of the Opera House in the arms of a
total stranger who seemed to know not only who she
was but what she did for a living!

She closed her eyes then opened them slowly again
but it made no difference. The man was still there, one
hard arm looped easily around her shoulders, his blond
head gleaming in the light from the chandeliers, his stag-
geringly handsome face set into lines of urbane charm
which somehow she *knew* was completely false. He was
the man who had come in through the doors before, the
one who had drawn all those lustful female eyes. Well,
as far as she was concerned they were welcome to him!

She sucked in a deep breath but once again the stranger
seemed to second-guess her intentions. He bent and
dropped a silencing kiss on her parted lips then slid his
mouth to her ear in a gesture which to anyone watching

must have looked purely affectionate but which had a deeper significance.

'I heard the message you left for Marcus. I decided you needed some help, so let me do my knight errant act, sweet, without any of those protests I can see you're dying to make.'

Natalie gasped. What did he mean, he'd heard the message she'd left? And why on earth should he imagine she wanted *his* help? However, before she could gather her scattered wits, Damian said stiffly, 'Well, I am pleased that you could make it, Mr...?'

'O'Rourke, Flynn O'Rourke. Don't tell me Natalie has been keeping me such a secret. I know we didn't intend for news of our relationship to get out, but...!' The man laughed again, hugging a speechless Natalie to his side so that her breast was crushed against the hard wall of his chest. She counted to ten...slowly, wanting the words to be perfect when they finally left her mouth. How dared he imply that he...that she...that they...? Oh!

She counted again, striving for control, but by the time she felt she'd achieved it Damian was nowhere in sight. There was just her and the man standing in the middle of the foyer and every scrap of control evaporated under the force of her anger.

'Just what do you think you are playing at? Why have you come? And how dare you kiss me like that?'

Flynn stepped back, staring calmly down at her in a way which made Natalie itch to do something dreadful like slap him. She tossed her long black hair over her shoulders, her black eyes sparkling with temper as she felt colour sweep under her flawless pale olive skin. Her mother had been Italian, a fiery woman who'd felt deeply about most things, but Natalie had always prided herself on the fact that she seemed to have escaped the Latin temperament while inheriting Sofia's beauty. However, perhaps she had been just a shade too complacent. She had never felt so furiously angry before and it was all thanks to him, Flynn O'Rourke—if that really was his name!

'It seemed the best thing to do at the time, Natalie. And I must confess it was no hardship slipping into the role of your admirer.'

There was cool amusement in that deep voice and Natalie took a step towards him. 'If I was meant to feel flattered then I'm afraid you'll be sadly disappointed to hear that I'm not. Frankly, Mr O'Rourke, I——'

He cut her off with a smile on his lips which mirrored the amusement she'd heard in his voice. 'Better make that Flynn. I imagine that Renshaw will find it odd, in the circumstances, if you keep calling me Mr O'Rourke.'

'There are no circumstances! I don't believe this. Just what does it take to get through to you that I didn't invite you here to start poking your nose into my affairs?' Natalie's temper had reached boiling-point, seething and bubbling, so that she took another step towards the infuriating man.

'But surely that is the object of all this?' Flynn arched an elegant golden brow, his smile never wavering even in the face of her anger. 'That Damian Renshaw should think you're having an affair so that he'll keep his hot hands to himself?'

'But not with you! Can't you understand that?' Natalie snapped.

Flynn folded his arms across his chest, studying Natalie calmly. 'Of course, but unfortunately Marcus couldn't be here so I decided to take his place.'

'What do you mean, he couldn't be here? Why not? Did he send you?'

Flynn shook his head. 'Not exactly. He's gone away, so when I heard your message I decided to come along and help out instead. I take it you didn't know he would be going anywhere?'

'I...no.' Natalie looked away, afraid of what he might see in her face. Marcus had made no mention of going away last time they had spoken. On the contrary, his last words to her had been that they must have a serious talk soon. She'd spent hours mulling that over, savouring the thought of what he might want to talk about! Now it came as a doubly bitter blow to learn that Marcus had gone away without letting her know first. It made a mockery of all the tender little hopes and aspirations she'd been nurturing since that conversation.

'I realise it must have surprised you to have me turning up, but surely it makes little difference so long as Renshaw gets the message? After all, that's the real point of the exercise, isn't it?' Flynn glanced round, ignoring Natalie's outraged gasp as he slid a hand under her elbow to steer her towards the door leading into the auditorium.

Natalie pushed all the painful thoughts from her mind and dug her heels into the plush red carpet, dragging herself free while she glared up into O'Rourke's handsome face. 'It makes a difference to me! I don't know you! I don't want to know you. I especially don't want anyone, and that includes Damian, to think that you and I are...are...'

It was odd how difficult it suddenly seemed to say one simple word as her eyes met those sea-green ones. Natalie had the craziest feeling that she was drowning as she looked up into them, could almost feel the water closing over her head. She fought for breath, striving to draw lungfuls of life-giving air, but each moment that ticked past saw her sinking deeper and deeper into those glittering depths.

'Lovers?' The man's voice was low, vibrant as he said the word she'd had such difficulty with, and Natalie shot back to the surface with a rush and gasped.

'Yes!'

'Fine.' Flynn grinned at her. 'I'll tell Renshaw the truth, shall I, just to clear up the misunderstanding?' He took a long, ground-eating stride towards the door and the attendant who was watching them with ill-concealed impatience. There were just minutes to go before the first aria and there was no one left in the foyer apart from Natalie and this infuriating, arrogant, self-...

She blanked the string of adjectives, realising she had something more important to deal with.

'Wait!' She caught hold of Flynn O'Rourke's arm and stopped him, then let him go at once, oddly disturbed by the feel of those lean, hard muscles under her fingers. 'If you tell Damian the truth he'll be furious. It will be such a blow to his ego to realise that I've been lying to him and why. You...I...' Natalie looked away from O'Rourke's face, curling her hands into fists so that her red-painted nails cut tiny crescents into her palms. He *knew* what a corner she was in, knew that telling Damian Renshaw the truth would mean losing the contract, but would he make it easier for her by admitting he understood? No way!

'Yes?' Flynn glanced at his watch then back at Natalie with a faintly quizzical smile which did little to conceal the amusement dancing in his eyes. 'I hate to hurry you, Natalie, but Renshaw isn't going to be pleased if I disturb him just as the show begins. Better to get the unpleasantness over with so that he can concentrate on enjoying himself afterwards.'

Natalie sucked in air so fast that her lungs burned. 'I don't want you to tell him anything and you damned well know why! Be it on your own head, Flynn O'Rourke! Whatever happens now it's your fault for pushing your nose in where it wasn't wanted!'

She swept past him, ignoring the icy glare from the attendant for daring to be so late to take her seat. She paused to regain control before joining Damian and looked back just in time to see Flynn O'Rourke following her through the door. He stopped to say something to the grey-haired dragon on guard at the doorway, and although Natalie couldn't hear what it was it was as though a miracle had occurred. From fire-breathing custodian to eyelash fluttering *femme fatale* was quite a transformation in the space of seconds!

Even as Natalie watched the woman hurried forward to lead them to Damian Renshaw's private box, thus saving them valuable seconds they would otherwise have wasted looking for it. Flynn O'Rourke rewarded the woman with a thousand-watt smile then solicitously steered her into the corridor when she seemed too dazzled to find the door. He seated Natalie on one of the plush chairs then took the one next to her, settling himself comfortably with one long leg crossed over the other as the lights dimmed and the curtain went up.

Natalie sat in the darkened enclosure, trying her hardest to concentrate as the opera unfolded, but it was impossible to concentrate on anything but the man at her side. She glanced over at him, colour surging under her skin when she found him watching her, an odd gleam in his eyes which could only be classed as speculative—but why? She looked hurriedly away, feeling uneasy for some reason she couldn't explain. Who was this Flynn O'Rourke? Pushy, arrogant interloper? Or knight in shining armour who knew every way in the story-book to fight dragons? She had met him less than ten minutes before, knew nothing at all about him, yet something told her that life wasn't going to be the same for her now that he had taken those first bold steps into it!

CHAPTER TWO

BY THE time the curtain came down for the first interval, Natalie's head was throbbing steadily. The music hadn't helped, the ponderous arias and thunderous choruses assaulting her senses. She had no idea what the story-line was. She'd been too intent on the man at her side, his blond hair gleaming like soft Welsh gold in the dim light, his slim but undeniably muscular body just an impression in the shadows, to work it out. She could only pray that Damian wouldn't expect her to contribute much to any discussion during the interval!

When Damian led the party out of the box Natalie tried to get a grip on herself. She was being ridiculous to allow Flynn O'Rourke to disturb her this way. She had always prided herself on being rational, capable of dealing with any situation in a logical manner. Men were no mystery to her: she accepted the interest they showed her because of her beauty and the unconscious allure she exuded without taking too much notice of it. Her looks were just a quirk of fate, a pleasant combining of genes, that was all. If anything, Flynn O'Rourke had showed slightly *less* interest in her than was usual on a first meeting, so it wasn't that which disturbed her. Yet even now, doing nothing more than just walking beside him, she was achingly conscious of him. Could it be the fact that he had aroused her temper more than any man had ever done in the whole of her twenty-three years?

Natalie grasped that explanation, oddly relieved to have found a reason. She liked to know the reason for things which happened in her life, flourished in an environment where limits were set and surprises kept to a minimum. In a way she was an odd mix, artistic without given to temperament, capable of coming up with startlingly original ideas yet equally capable of realising when something tried and tested would work better. It was what made her so good at her job, what was taking her steadily up the ladder in the cut-throat world of advertising, and no one, especially not this infuriating stranger, was going to put that at risk!

'Penny for them—or perhaps it should be a pound? Thoughts as weighty as those running through your head, Natalie, must be worth that amount.'

Flynn O'Rourke's amused tones cut into Natalie's musings and she turned to stare coldly at him. 'You don't need to pay me. I'll tell you for free what I was thinking about: you!'

Flynn's eyes narrowed but he said nothing as he beckoned to the waiter who was circulating with a tray of drinks. He handed Natalie a glass of champagne then requested tonic water and ice for himself. Natalie sipped the dancing bubbles, seething inwardly as O'Rourke waited until the waiter had returned with his drink before saying calmly, 'As I don't imagine that you were paying me a compliment, why don't you tell me what's wrong now, before your friend Renshaw starts getting suspicious? Glaring at me like that is a real give-away, darling.'

'Don't you "darling" me, O'Rourke! I'm not your darling, I'm not your anything! Understand?' Natalie's fingers curled round the stem of the glass as she fought to control the fresh waves of temper. She took a sip of the drink then fixed a smile to her lips as she caught Damian's eye across the crowd. He raised his glass aloft in a courtly toast which she acknowledged with a dip of her head before letting her gaze return to the man before her, and felt a *frisson* run down her spine when she saw the ice in his green eyes.

He bent towards her until his golden head was mere inches from hers, his voice a low rumble which made the shudders intensify although she couldn't really have explained why. 'I understand that you're a friend of Marcus's, a friend who was desperate enough to ring him and beg him to meet you here tonight. I heard the call you made, Natalie, because I'm staying in Marcus's flat while he's away, so I thought to myself, Why not repay the favour he's done me? Why not go along and help out Marcus's old friend, seeing as he can't be there? But obviously I was wrong to do so.'

Natalie glanced at her glass, feeling like an ungrateful wretch. Put like that, Flynn O'Rourke's decision to come tonight seemed generous and unselfish and... If she hadn't chanced to glance up right then and see the gleam of calculation in the aqua depths of his eyes she might have continued heaping praise upon O'Rourke's golden head and ashes upon her own. But one glance was all it took to set her straight. He had done it deliberately, played upon her guilt for his own miserable ends!

'Why you no-good——!'

'Not interrupting, am I, Natalie?' Damian's rather high voice cut off the less than complimentary string of names she'd been struggling with. Natalie took a deep breath then turned to smile brightly at her host.

'Of course not, Damian.' She shot a mean look at O'Rourke then smoothed the smile back into place as she focused on the other man. 'We were just discussing the opera.'

'Were you?' Damian gave a small laugh. 'Funny, but from across the room I could have sworn that you two were quarrelling. But that goes to show how wrong one can be.' He turned to Flynn, his eyes cold as they centred on him. 'I do hope you aren't finding the evening too boring. Opera isn't everyone's taste, I know.'

'Not at all. "Boring" isn't the adjective which springs to mind when Natalie is around. I always find that being with her is a pleasure in itself.'

Natalie bit back the hot retort, trying to remember that O'Rourke was only acting a part—very badly, granted, but just the role as he saw it.

'Of course.' Damian's voice was icy, his eyes pebble-hard as they lifted several inches to meet the green ones which were regarding him just as coolly. 'But even Natalie's charming company might not be enough if you aren't a true *aficionado*.'

'Perhaps not of this particular work...' Flynn shrugged lightly.

'I can understand that,' Damian said pompously, looking smugly superior. 'It isn't the easiest work to follow, but rewarding nevertheless for those who appreciate such things.'

Flynn took a sip of his tonic water then swirled the ice around his glass in a musical tinkle, an expression on his face which Natalie found hard to define but which immediately made her go tense. Behind that lazy, laid-back charm she caught a glimpse of something else...the real Flynn O'Rourke?...and something warned her that Damian was about to see it too.

'As you undoubtedly do, Renshaw? Of course I found the production put on at La Scala last autumn more to my taste. But then one can never fault Caballe's voice and the presence she brings to a role, don't you think?

Perhaps you were lucky enough to catch it?' Flynn
O'Rourke's voice was just as low, just as easy as always,
but Natalie winced at every word. Damian Renshaw
considered himself a patron of the arts, and an expert
in his chosen field of opera. He wouldn't be pleased to
be thrown such an indisputable challenge!

Two bright spots of ugly colour glowed on his fleshy
cheeks. 'Unfortunately, no. It seems that you and I have
more than just Natalie in common, O'Rourke, although
I must say that she has been remarkably reticent about
you. What sort of line are you in?'

Flynn tipped his head back and drained the glass, then
carefully set it down on a passing waiter's tray. 'Oh, this
and that. You know how it is.'

'Of course.' Damian cast Natalie a faintly triumphant
look, letting her know what he thought of a man who
did 'this and that' to earn a living. 'What exactly are
you working on at present?' he asked loftily.

'Right now I'm hoping to take a holiday and do as
little as possible—apart from seeing a lot of Natalie, that
is,' Flynn replied smoothly. He slid his arm around
Natalie's waist and drew her to his side, holding her so
close that despite her stiffness she found herself moulded
to the length of his lean body. 'After that I'll see what
turns up.'

'I see.' Damian's good humour seemed somewhat restored as he patted Natalie's hand. 'Well, I must cir-
culate. I'll speak to you later. We're all going on to supper
at Annabel's afterwards, if you would care to join us?'

Natalie opened her mouth to make some sort of
excuse, unable to face the thought of much more. Didn't
O'Rourke realise that he was antagonising Damian, and
that that was the last thing she wanted at this delicate
stage in negotiations? 'I'm sor——'

Flynn cut her off, his deeper tones drowning hers out. 'I'm afraid Natalie and I have other plans for later, Renshaw.' He dropped his gaze to her face, smiling into her eyes as he said softly, 'Haven't we, darling?'

Natalie couldn't help herself. She could feel the blush starting at the base of her throat, feel it creeping in a hot tide under her skin. It was the way Flynn O'Rourke was looking at her, his sea-green eyes *smouldering*, his mouth curved into the sexiest smile she'd ever seen. When he bent and brushed her mouth with the gentlest of kisses, she actually sighed before suddenly coming to her senses.

She shook him off like a dog shaking off water after an unwanted dip, glad that Damian had moved away to speak to another guest. 'Just what do you think you are playing at, O'Rourke?' she gritted out from between tightly clenched teeth.

Flynn shot a glance over his shoulder then steered Natalie behind one of the marble pillars, leaning an indolent shoulder against it as he stared quizzically at her with a faint lift of one elegant brow. 'Convincing Renshaw that you and I are, as the Americans call it, an "item". That's what you wanted, wasn't it? I distinctly recall you begging Marcus to—I quote—"do your best to convince Damian he's wasting his time". Now maybe I've got my motivation for the role slightly wrong but I thought I was doing one hell of a job just now.'

'Let's cut out the smart answers! You know very well that I was expecting Marcus to come tonight, not some . . . some *interloper*! Any instructions I left on that machine were meant for him, and him alone!' She could feel her temper moving rapidly up the scale from merely hot to volcanic, and it shocked her. True, it hurt to know that Marcus had gone away without telling her, but could

that really explain how she was feeling now, this red-hot
anger? So what if Flynn O'Rourke was the most infuriating man she'd ever met? Why didn't she respond
as she usually did with a persistent male and just treat
him with cool indifference? Yet somehow it seemed impossible to apply those tactics to him!

'Then all I can do is apologise. Perhaps I have been
a shade too...enthusiastic, shall we say? But it was with
the best of intentions, you understand, Natalie. I only
wanted to help a lady in distress, and a close friend of
Marcus's at that.'

This time Natalie didn't repeat the mistake she'd made
earlier. Before starting to berate herself for being ungrateful, she looked long and hard at O'Rourke, but she
could see no signs this time of any cunning calculation.
She sighed wearily, smoothing a heavy black wave behind
her ear as she forced herself to smile. 'Perhaps I do owe
you an apology, Mr...Flynn,' she amended quickly. 'It
was kind of you to come to try to help me out and I am
sorry if I appear unappreciative of the trouble you've
gone to.'

'Don't give it a second thought.' Flynn raised his hand
and smoothed a stray wisp of hair she'd missed behind
her ear, his fingers lingering just a moment longer than
was strictly necessary, cool and hard against her warm
flesh. Natalie shivered at the touch of his hand but before
she could make any move to break the contact he did
so. 'As for it being any trouble...well, frankly, I wouldn't
have missed a moment of tonight for many reasons.' His
smile deepened as his gaze lingered on Natalie's up-
turned face and she felt again that faint unease at the
hint of speculation in the glittering green depths of his
eyes, before he continued in a voice as smooth as silk,

'Not least of which was the feeling I had that you would come to appreciate me eventually.'

The unease faded, wiped out by those silky smooth words which had the impact of a bullet as they hit home. Natalie took a furious step back, realising that once again the wretched man had tricked her into feeling guilty!

She swung round on her heel just as the bell rang to warn people that the interval was nearly over, marching back to her seat without a backward glance to see if O'Rourke was following her. Yet when he did enter the box a few minutes later she couldn't resist shooting him a wary look. She had always believed that there was a reason for everything that happened, but what reason could fate have had for sending Flynn O'Rourke into her life? And why did she have the strangest feeling that it hadn't merely been some odd little hiccup in life's otherwise smooth path? It was all highly unsettling.

It was raining when they left the Opera House, the late April sky black as pitch. Natalie's headache had reached gigantic proportions now, thundering like a demented percussionist. She pushed her way through the crowd on the steps, barely glancing at the line of gleaming limousines arriving to collect their wealthy owners. Somewhere among the line-up would be Damian's Rolls but Natalie didn't experience even a twinge of regret that she wouldn't be going home in it. Frankly, the sooner this night was over the better!

'If we're entered in a race then you should have warned me. I'd have made certain I was on the starting-line beside you then.'

Flynn O'Rourke's coolly amused tones brought Natalie to a dead stop. She turned to glare at him, uncaring that rain was streaming down her face or that the silk suit which had cost the best part of a month's salary would never look the same again after its soaking. She had said a curt goodbye to O'Rourke as soon as they had parted from the others, but perhaps she hadn't made her meaning perfectly plain!

'Goodnight, Mr O'Rourke,' she said coldly. 'I can't say that it has been a pleasure meeting you but it has been an experience—one I shall try my hardest to forget!'

She hurried on, trying her best to ignore the fact that O'Rourke was strolling alongside her. She wouldn't look at him, wouldn't give him *any* encouragement. But it proved as impossible to ignore him now as it had been earlier.

Natalie slid a glance his way from under her lashes, noting how the rain had darkened his hair to old gold. It lay sleekly against his head, emphasising the elegant purity of his profile. He had his hands pushed into his trouser pockets, uncaring, it seemed, that the action had parted the front of his black dinner-jacket so that the rain was soaking into the thin fabric of his shirt, to turn it almost transparent. As they passed beneath a street-lamp Natalie could see the wedge of hair over his breastbone, the taut lines of every perfectly defined muscle in his chest. She looked away at once, strangely disturbed by the sight and furious with herself for feeling that way.

'What does it take to get rid of you?' she demanded waspishly.

Flynn flicked her a glance, amusement dancing in his eyes. 'I assume by that that you think I'm following you?'

'No, of course not! I mean to say, here you are walking no more than a few feet away from me, so why on earth should I make such a hasty assumption?'

He laughed softly, slowing his pace to keep level with her as they weaved through a group of merry-makers leaving a pub. One of the men leered at Natalie, then sobered instantly and turned away when Flynn took her arm and gave him a look which could have stopped traffic. Natalie waited until they were out of earshot of the group then wrenched her arm from his grasp.

'Look, I don't know if you have some misguided idea about seeing me safely home, but I assure you I can manage perfectly well by myself. So please do us both a favour and go away!'

'I would love to comply, Natalie, but unfortunately the simple truth is that we both seem to be heading in the same direction.' He raised both brows when she stared at him with disbelief. 'The taxi rank?'

Natalie gritted her teeth, nodding curtly as she carried on walking. It was such a perfectly reasonable explanation, but one thing she *had* learned about O'Rourke was just how plausible he could be! She wouldn't put it past him to have left his car somewhere and made up that excuse on the spur of the moment!

'From what I heard on that message you left, you and Marcus seem to be old friends?'

She didn't spare him a glance, refusing to be drawn into making conversation, especially about Marcus! 'Yes.'

'You must know him well, then?'

'Yes.'

'I expect you've met a lot of the people he deals with, then?'

She paused in mid-stride, shaking the rain out of her eyes. 'What is this, O'Rourke? Twenty questions? Why are you so interested in my relationship with Marcus?'

'Relationship? I see.'

There was a note in his voice which made her toes curl. Natalie carried on down the street, quickening her pace, but he kept in step with her. The choice of the word 'relationship' had been a Freudian slip but she wasn't going to explain that to him!

'It's odd but I can't recall Marcus ever mentioning you,' O'Rourke mused. 'I'm sure I would have remembered but I can't recall him ever saying a word about you, yet you and he are old...friends?'

She wouldn't let him see how much that hurt. Why should Marcus mention her? Yet on the other hand if she'd meant as much to him as he did to her then surely her name would have cropped up in conversation? It was yet another painful reminder that she had been building dreams on shifting sands for years now, and Natalie couldn't quite keep the bite from her voice as she responded to a statement which had touched a raw nerve. 'I don't remember him mentioning you either! It makes me wonder just how close a friend of Marcus you are.'

'Did I say we were friends?' He gave a short, oddly harsh laugh. 'I don't recall it.'

Natalie stopped, her face mirroring her confusion. 'Then why on earth is he allowing you to stay in his flat?' She paused, struck by a sudden thought. 'He does know that you're there!'

'Of course. Perhaps I didn't make myself clear. Marcus and I are business associates rather than friends in the strict sense of the word. I wish you could call him to put your mind at rest but...' He shrugged indifferently yet there was an intentness to the look he treated Natalie to which belied that. 'He told me that he would be away for a couple of weeks. I don't suppose you have any idea where he's gone to, just in case anything crops up in the future?'

Natalie looked away, carefully keeping her voice level so that he would get no inkling of how much it hurt to admit that she had no idea at all. 'If I had then I would hardly have gone to the trouble of telephoning him earlier, would I?'

'No, of course not. I should have thought of that before.' He glanced at the sky and gave a rueful grimace. 'Come on, we'd better hurry up before all the taxis are commandeered. Hopefully there'll be one at the rank.' He slid his hand under her elbow but Natalie shook him off.

'One? Don't you mean *two*? If you imagine that I am sharing a taxi with you, O'Rourke, then think again! I've had just about enough of you tonight to last me a lifetime!'

Her temper, which had been pushed to its limit in the past few hours, spiralled, and she bit back a groan at the resulting pounding in her temples. It had been ages since she'd had a headache like this, although in her teens she had been prone to migraine attacks and she had the suspicion that this was turning into one now.

Even as she thought it she could see the flashes of colour at the perimeter of her vision which always presaged an attack. She closed her eyes to try to ward it off but the flashes were rapidly gathering strength.

'Are you all right? Here, lean on me.'

Flynn O'Rourke's deep voice sounded wonderfully reassuring, the feel of his hard body even more so as he looped his arm around her waist and supported her. He smoothed her wet hair back from her face then nestled her head into the hollow of his shoulder. For a weak moment Natalie was tempted to let him take charge but she refused to show weakness in front of the one person responsible for her present state!

She pushed him away, swaying slightly as she faced him. 'Don't! Perhaps some women of your acquaintance enjoy those macho tactics, O'Rourke, but I don't. So spare me. I can manage without any help from you!'

He stepped back, studying her with a faint curl of his chiselled lips. 'Most *people* of my acquaintance are sensible enough to accept help when they need it. But if you prefer to go it alone, honey, then feel free. I'll see you around some day... perhaps.'

He walked off, his long legs eating up the ground as he disappeared into the night. Natalie watched him go with a sense of disbelief. It seemed out of character for him to leave with so little objection, but there again what did she know about the damnable man's character?

Pushing the thought to the back of her mind, she carried on, but with each step knew that the migraine was getting worse, her vision blurring now so that she had difficulty in focusing. Pausing for a moment, she hung on to a lamp-post and screwed up her eyes while she tried to measure the distance to the taxi rank, but it seemed such a long way even now. Perhaps she should have accepted O'Rourke's offer to help after all?

'Need a hand, darlin'? Looks like you could do with it, seeing as your boyfriend has ditched you.'

Natalie's heart lurched as she recognised the three men, who formed a small circle around her, as the ones from the pub. She shaped her mouth into what she hoped was a confident smile. 'I'm fine, thank you.'

'You don't look it, love. Looks to me like you've had a drop too much, and we know just how that feels, don't we, lads?'

They all laughed, but Natalie was in no mood to share the joke. She drew herself up and stared haughtily at them. 'I've already told you that I don't need your help, so please go away.'

An unpleasant expression crept across the spokesman's face as he took a threatening step towards her. 'That isn't very nice, lady. Me and my mates here make a genuine offer to help and what do we get...insults?'

He reached out and Natalie shrank away, but before he could touch her the oddest thing happened. One minute the man was standing there blasting her with his beery breath and the next he was crashing to the pavement.

'I believe you heard the lady. She doesn't need your help. If you're having trouble understanding her then maybe I can make it a bit plainer?'

Flynn O'Rourke was suddenly there, his voice holding a note of pure steel which made even Natalie shiver. It seemed to have a marked effect on her would-be helpers because even as she watched the other two lifted the third from the ground and hurriedly led him away.

Natalie raised a dazed face to O'Rourke, squinting as she tried to see him properly, but the light from the streetlamps bouncing off his golden hair made her head ache. She closed her eyes on a wave of pain then gasped when she felt herself being lifted off the ground.

'What...what do you think you're doing?' she managed to croak.

Flynn strode over to the waiting taxi and lowered her to the seat before getting in beside her and slamming the door. 'What any sane man should have done before—making you see sense!'

It was the most chauvinistic thing Natalie had ever heard! She tried to glare at him but it proved impossible

when there seemed to be at least ten of him printed on
her eyeballs. He obviously got the message, however,
because she heard him laugh, the sound rumbling inside
his chest under her ear, the vibrations making her tingle
alarmingly. He cupped her cheek, the warmth of his palm
and the faint roughness of his skin setting up a whole
fresh chain of unsettling reactions.

'Later, Natalie. You can tell me exactly what you think
later.'

Oh, she would. She would most definitely leave Flynn
O'Rourke in no doubt as to her feelings! He was the
most impossible, arrogant, self-opinionated man she'd
ever had the misfortune to meet and she would tell him
that . . . later. For now it seemed enough to let him just
take charge of the situation. It was funny, but she had
the feeling that it was something he was well-used
to doing.

CHAPTER THREE

MORNING sunshine was bathing the bedroom in a soft apricot light when Natalie awoke. She lay for a moment, savouring the sense of relief which always followed the end of a migraine attack, then let her gaze move to the photograph on the bedside table. She had put it there specifically for that purpose, so that when she woke she could look at it and see Marcus.

She'd begged the print off Becky, Marcus's sister, a couple of years before, making up some excuse about wanting it as a memento of a lovely day. It had been taken when the three of them had spent the day at London Zoo, a day which even now Natalie could recall with vivid clarity. It had been that day when she had finally admitted to herself that she loved Marcus Cole.

Natalie let her mind drift back over the years to when she had first met him, although it was hard to remember when Marcus hadn't been an integral part of her life. She'd been seventeen when Becky had invited her home to tea that first time. Natalie had just moved into the area and was desperately unhappy. Her parents had been killed in a tragic road accident and she had been sent to live with an elderly aunt of her father's whom she'd never even met before. It had meant leaving her home and all her friends to find herself the outsider in the close-knit village community. Becky's offer of friendship had been a lifeline in a world which had changed so drastically.

So she had gone to the Coles' house and there was Marcus, ten years older than his sister and Natalie, a sophisticated man whose dark good looks had cast a spell over her immediately. The problem was that Marcus apparently didn't reciprocate her feelings! He treated Natalie the same way he treated his sister but, short of confessing to him how she felt and running the risk of losing his friendship because he might be horribly embarrassed, there'd seemed little she could do. Yet recently she'd sensed a change in his attitude. Was it possible that Marcus was beginning to see her in a different light? It had been that hope as much as the need to solve the problem of Damian's interest which had made her invite him last night, the idea that seeing another man pursuing her might jolt Marcus into examining his own feelings, yet look how it had turned out!

Thoughts of the previous evening and what had happened had her tossing back the quilt in a sudden surge of anger. Last night was over and she wouldn't think about it again, let alone allow herself to dwell on *that* man!

Dragging on her old red robe, she headed for the kitchen, determined to put last night behind her although what had happened once she'd got in the taxi was hazy, thanks to the migraine. The rest was crystal-clear, though, right from the moment O'Rourke had appeared and kissed her up to the very second he had walked off and left her in the rain. If they handed out awards for the most infuriating man who'd ever walked the earth then Flynn O'Rourke just had to be the number one contender!

Pushing open the kitchen door, Natalie came to an abrupt halt. For a moment she couldn't seem to move, let alone speak, her gaze locked to the man standing by the stove. In an incredulous sweep her eyes ran from the top of his blond head over the leanly muscular lines of his naked chest, the narrow hips encased in black trousers to his elegant bare feet, scarcely able to believe what she was seeing. But then he turned to smile at her, his sea-green eyes dancing with amusement, and she realised he was only too real!

'Morning, Natalie. How do you feel today? Can you manage some breakfast?' Muscles rippled as he bent to open the fridge and take out a handful of eggs, watching her with an interest which suddenly warned her what kind of expression he might be seeing on her face!

Hurriedly she looked away from the sight of all that gorgeous tanned flesh and drew in a breath to compensate for the one or two she'd missed. 'Just what do you think you are doing?' she demanded.

Flynn raised a quizzical eyebrow, deftly breaking eggs into a bowl before starting to beat them. 'Making breakfast, of course. Scrambled all right for you too, Natalie?'

'Cut it out, O'Rourke! You know very well I'm not talking about what you're doing in the kitchen but what you're doing in my home!' Natalie marched over to him and snatched the beater from his hand so fast that egg spattered in several directions. Some of it landed on Flynn's bare chest and he grimaced as he ran his hand over the sticky droplets, immediately drawing Natalie's unwilling attention to the width of his shoulders, the thick golden hair which arrowed down to his belt. There wasn't an ounce of spare flesh on his body, as Natalie could have testified to any jury, and hurriedly she averted her gaze to the comparative safety of his face. 'Well?'

'Are you always this tetchy of a morning? Or is it just the aftermath of that headache?' Flynn calmly took the beater back and went to work on the eggs again.

Natalie summoned up patience, trying her best to remember that she was noted for her calmness, her control,
her ability to handle even the most taxing situation. But
never had she come across anyone as taxing as he! 'I
shall give you precisely one minute, O'Rourke. Sixty tiny
little seconds to come up with an answer, and if you
don't then I shall...I shall...'

What on earth could she threaten him with? Her mind
went blank, every brain cell fading like a burned-out
microchip as Flynn O'Rourke calmly slid his hands
around her waist and lifted her as easily as though she
were a child then set her gently down on one of the an-
tique pine chairs around the table.

He took a napkin from the place-setting and shook it
out then dropped it on to her lap, his green eyes dancing
with devilish laughter. 'You just sit there and think about
it, Natalie. I'm sure you'll come up with something in
a moment or two. In the meantime I'll go and get those
eggs started.'

He went back to the stove, working confidently as he
stirred the eggs into a hot pan. They were cooked in
minutes, creamy-smooth and golden when he tipped
them on to two plates and carried them back to the table.
Setting one in front of Natalie, he sat down and picked
up a fork, eating with obvious enjoyment before glancing
up at her solicitously. 'You really should try them, honey.
Might help you think up a really effective threat.'

Natalie pushed the plate away and shoved back her
chair. 'I don't need anything to help me do that! I am
going straight into the sitting-room and phoning the
police to tell them that a man has forced his way into
my flat and refuses to leave!'

'Forced?' Flynn forked up another mouthful of eggs and chewed it slowly, watching her without a flicker of alarm at the threat. 'Are you quite sure of your facts?'

'Of course I am! I didn't invite you in here!' She tried to add a note of conviction to her voice but saw by the way he smiled that she hadn't been wholly successful. If only she could remember what had happened after she'd got into that taxi...

'I'd say that handing me the key to the door could be construed as an invitation, but perhaps you don't remember that, the same as you don't remember the rest of it?' Flynn scooped up the last forkful of eggs then sat back in the chair, an expression on his handsome face which made Natalie long to wipe it away.

'The rest of it?' She laughed lightly, inwardly wincing at the hint of strain in the sound. 'Come on, O'Rourke! You don't really expect me to believe that something happened between you and me?'

'Did I imply that?' He smiled easily, white teeth gleaming against tanned skin. Even with a night's growth of beard and his hair mussed he was still sinfully handsome—but Natalie was immune to his looks, she told herself severely.

'Yes! You know you did. Now either tell me what you're hinting at or...'

'Or... what? You will go call the police? I don't think they'd be too pleased to have their valuable time wasted, sweet.' He put his hands behind his head and arched his back, grimacing slightly. 'That sofa of yours isn't the most comfortable of spots to spend the night.'

Well, at least that answered one disturbing little question, although Natalie was certain that she would have remembered if O'Rourke had shared her bed, no matter how dazed she'd been by the headache!

She smiled with saccharine sweetness at him. 'Oh, dear! But you only have yourself to blame. Nobody asked you to use it, the same as nobody invited you to stay, so why did you? Come on, O'Rourke, let's hear it.'

Her patience was waning by the second, eroding away with his mocking taunts and, if she was honest, with the strange reactions her body kept giving. She didn't like Flynn O'Rourke; he was a perfect nuisance who had done nothing but disrupt her life since he'd had the temerity to force his way into it. Yet that didn't explain the odd little shivers running races up and down her spine, the hot tingles of awareness she experienced as she looked at him lounging there in her kitchen chair!

His smile faded abruptly, his green eyes cooler than Arctic ice as they rested on her face. 'You want to loosen up a bit, Natalie, and not take everything, yourself included, so seriously. The plain truth is that you weren't in any fit state to be left by yourself last night so I decided to stay here to keep an eye on you. That's it. No great mystery, and no, I most definitely didn't attempt to have my wicked way with you.'

He made it sound so ridiculous, like something out of a Victorian novel, and her face flamed but she stood her ground. 'It would be a cold day in hell before that happened, O'Rourke!'

He was up out of the chair and around the table before she could gasp out a protest. Catching her chin in one lean hand, he bent to stare into her startled black eyes. 'I wouldn't be quite so sure of that. Tossing out that kind of a challenge to a man is a sure way to make him want to prove you wrong.'

'It wasn't meant to be a challenge!' She caught her breath and twisted herself free from the disturbing contact with his hand, her eyes blazing with anger. 'Don't bother giving me all that macho rubbish, because I'm not interested!'

'Macho? And last night it was chauvinistic? You don't seem to hold a very high opinion of me, Natalie, and after all the trouble I went to last night...'

'You probably only did it for your own ends!' she flung back at him.

'And what do you mean by that?' His eyes narrowed, coldly assessing, sending a chill through her body. She had the sudden feeling that she had touched a nerve but unfortunately didn't know which one so couldn't touch it again!

'That you probably stayed not to help me, as you claim, but just so you could bait me this morning. It seems to give you no end of pleasure!'

He grinned lazily, folding his arms across his chest as he studied her furious face and sparkling eyes. 'And there was I doing my Good Samaritan act... You wound me, my sweet.'

'Good! I wish I could do it a bit more effectively, leave you in no doubt about the fact that I want you out of my home and out of my life just as soon as humanly possible!'

'In that case there doesn't seem an awful lot left to say, does there?' He strode past her, walking unhurriedly into the sitting-room to pick up his shirt from where it was draped over the back of a chair and slip it on. He buttoned it partway then sat down to slip his feet into his shoes, rolling the black silk socks into a ball and pushing them into his pocket. Picking up his jacket from the arm of the sofa, he hooked a finger in the collar and swung it over his shoulder, then glanced over at where Natalie was standing, silently watching.

'Right, that's it, then. Thank you for your hospitality but take my advice and invest in a bigger sofa. That one is death for any guest's back unless they're a midget.'

Natalie bit down hard on the retort. Guests were people who were *invited* to stay and O'Rourke didn't fall into that category. However, it seemed prudent not to prolong his leaving by arguing over such a technicality so she merely watched as he walked to the door. He glanced back at her with a mocking smile.

'Aren't you coming to wave me off, Natalie?'

Natalie smiled tightly back at him as she marched into the hall and opened the front door. 'But of course. I wouldn't want to miss doing that for anything.'

Flynn laughed deeply, his voice holding a rumble of amusement. 'It's been good meeting you, Natalie. I have really enjoyed it, believe me. If I didn't have the strongest suspicion that you would refuse I would be tempted to suggest we do it again soon.'

Natalie's fingers curled around the edge of the door as she hung on to her temper. 'How well you are starting to know me.'

'Oh, not half so well as I would like to.' He bent and brushed a kiss over her cheek, drawing back before she could frame a protest. He grinned at her furious expression, flicking a finger softly against her mouth. 'No, don't say it, Natalie. Let's not spoil this tender moment.'

Natalie's fingers were locked in a death-grip on the wood because she was afraid to release them in case she did something dreadful! 'If you have quite finished...' She inched the door over, wanting only to be rid of him before he did or said anything else. However, he stopped her from closing it with a hand against the wooden panels.

'Not quite. I almost forgot. You had a visitor last night.'

'A visitor... Marcus?' There was a note of eagerness in the question that she hadn't meant O'Rourke to hear and she felt colour run under her skin at the openly assessing expression in his green eyes.

'Sorry to disappoint you but no, it wasn't Marcus. I think I told you that he intends to be away for a couple of weeks—unless you know differently, of course?'

What was there in his deep voice now—a certain harshness which turned what should have been nothing more than a passing remark into a question? Natalie shrugged but didn't answer, more concerned with finding out who the visitor had been than working it out, and after a moment Flynn continued smoothly.

'Actually it was your boss—Guy, I think he said his name was.'

'Guy? But what did he want? Why didn't you get me?'

Flynn shrugged dismissively. 'You were dead to the world so I didn't see any point. Frankly, I doubt if you would have been in any fit state to discuss business.'

'I would have preferred to be the judge of that! Honestly, O'Rourke, what gave you the right to make that kind of decision for me?' She bit off the rest of the tirade, taking a deep breath to steady herself. Arguing was only prolonging this, and that was the last thing she wanted. 'Did Guy leave a message?'

'No. In the end he decided to leave it until he saw you today. I must say he seemed a pleasant enough character.'

Natalie smiled tightly. 'I'm sure he will be eternally grateful for that compliment. Now, if that's it...'

'It is apart from where I put your clothes.'

'Where you put my clothes?' Natalie's voice rose and she looked away from the green eyes which were glit-

tering with undisguised amusement, heat suffusing her
when suddenly she spotted the elderly woman who lived
in the next flat.

'Mmm, yes. They were soaked through so once we'd
got you undressed I hung them in the bathroom to dry
off.' Flynn's voice seemed to echo around the small
hallway, the deep tones resonant with meaning. Natalie
just had a chance to glimpse the expression on her
neighbour's face before the woman closed her door, but
it was enough to tell her how it had sounded!

'Why, you...you...!' She knew exactly what she
wanted to say, could hear each word clearly inside her
head, but her mouth refused to frame them. And while
Natalie struggled Flynn bent and patted her cheek.

'Thanks for a really wonderful night, honey.'

He was gone before she could stop him, before she
could give voice to all those angry words. Instead Natalie
had to content herself with slamming the door. Swinging
round on her heel, she marched into the bedroom and
picked up the photograph and stared at it. It was a tried
and tested method of soothing her nerves, although she
didn't recall ever feeling this angry before! Yet for some
reason the magic didn't work this time.

She concentrated harder on Marcus's familiar features, his dark hair, the straight nose, that fascinating
cleft in his chin...

The picture started to blur around the edges and
Natalie blinked rapidly to dispel the fresh one which was
replacing it, but it proved as impossible to rid herself of
the man's image as it had been to rid herself of the flesh-
and blood version. Blond hair, dancing aqua eyes, a face
so handsome it might have come from a painting...
Flynn O'Rourke was stepping into her mind just as easily
as last night he had stepped into her life!

* * *

If anyone had told her twelve hours ago that she would be doing this then Natalie would have told them they were crazy. But a lot could happen in a few short hours, as she knew to her cost!

Slamming the car door, she strode into the entrance of the imposing block of flats. It was empty apart from the porter on duty behind the desk. He nodded to Natalie but made no attempt to stop her as she made her way to the lifts. Over the past couple of years she'd been a regular visitor to the building as she and Marcus had shared the odd, companionable dinner in his flat. She posed no threat to the residents or their property in his view. If only the man had some idea what she would like to do to one *particular* resident then maybe he wouldn't be so complacent!

Lips compressed, Natalie set the lift on course for the third floor. When the doors glided open she didn't hesitate, her footsteps muffled by the thick grey tweed carpet as she strode across the hall and rapped on a door; but there was no answer. She knocked again, louder this time, her impatience rising. If he was out...

'Yes? Natalie! What a lovely surprise. Do come in.' Flynn O'Rourke was suddenly there, mouth curving into a mockingly familiar smile as he saw the shock on her face. He glanced down at the white towel wrapped around his hips, the only item of clothing he was wearing, then said smoothly, 'You got me out of the shower.'

Natalie stalked past him, trying her hardest to ignore all that gleaming wet skin, the aroma of soap and shampoo which clung so enticingly to him. 'So I see. Unfortunately I need to speak to you, though.'

'Do you? Sounds interesting.' He closed the door then waved a hand towards the sitting-room. 'Why don't you make yourself comfortable while I get dressed?'

Natalie would have loved to tell him not to bother but the thought of conducting a conversation with O'Rourke in that state was more than she could cope with.

She walked into the familiar room, feeling a tug of pain that Marcus wasn't there. She'd heard nothing from him, but then why should she? He had no obligation to tell her of his whereabouts, but it still hurt that he had gone away without so much as a word to her first.

'Can I get you anything—a drink or coffee, perhaps?' Flynn's arrival in the room cut off the painful line of thought. Natalie turned to look at him with a relief which only lasted a second or so. He'd dressed in well-washed jeans which clung lovingly to his long legs and a white shirt with the sleeves rolled up to his elbows, casual clothes yet he looked just as elegant and stunning in them as he had done in the black dinner-jacket. Natalie was suddenly intensely conscious of the fact that she'd come straight from the office without bothering to change out of her usual garb of knee-length black skirt and silky knit sweater. She hadn't even run a brush through the snarls in her black hair and she suddenly wished that she'd taken time to change into an outfit which would have given a boost to her confidence. But there again this wasn't a social visit; it was strictly business! she quickly told herself.

'Nothing, thank you,' she replied shortly.

'Why do I get the feeling that you're upset?'

'Probably because I am!' She swung round to walk to the window, trying hard to stay calm, but now that she was here and O'Rourke was just a few feet away that seemed the hardest thing in the world to do!

'Why don't you start at the beginning and tell me what's wrong?' Flynn's voice was deliberately reasonable, the deep tones meant to be soothing, but all they did was set a light to her temper.

'You know what's wrong! Why did you do it? Just tell me that!' She swung round to glare at him, tossing back the long strands of hair as they swirled around her shoulders.

He sat down on one of the black leather chairs, regarding her quizzically. 'I'd be happy to if you would just give me a clue as to what it is I'm supposed to have done.'

'*Supposed*? There's no supposed about it. It was done deliberately! Cold, calculated and *deliberate* interference—poking your nose in where it wasn't wanted yet again!'

Flynn sighed, steepling his fingers to stare at her over the top of them. 'I can't for the life of me imagine what it is, so perhaps I had better run through all the possibilities. I didn't lay a finger on you last night so that rules out any future repercussions.' He ignored Natalie's gasp of outrage, a pensive look on his face as he ticked off his fingers. 'I don't think I left anything behind, nor did I help myself to your silver, so that's two and three dispensed with. So what else could it be?'

She must have been mad to imagine that they could talk about this rationally! Natalie strode back across the room, her eyes flashing with temper, but Flynn merely rested his head back against the cushion and regarded her levelly.

'If I have created some sort of a problem for you then I want to know what it is.' There was no mockery in his voice now, just a steely hardness she'd heard once before. Natalie hesitated, trying to reconcile this cold-eyed stranger with the man whose mockery had made last night an unforgettable experience. On the surface Flynn

O'Rourke seemed to treat life casually, with an almost throw-away attitude, but was that merely a way to disguise that underneath that laughing, charming façade lay a man who was tough to the core?

'Natalie?'

The stern note in his voice roused her and she looked away from eyes which suddenly seemed far too discerning. 'If you hadn't——'

He cut her off smoothly. 'Poked my nose in. Yes, I know, so let's not waste time rehashing old grievances.' He got up and walked over to the table where there was a pot of coffee standing on a tray. He poured a cup then carried it back and offered it to her. 'Drink this and tell me what's wrong.'

Natalie took the cup from him but made no attempt to drink it. She glared back at him from stormy black eyes. '*This* grievance is perfectly fresh! Just what did you and Guy talk about when he came to my flat last night?'

Flynn raised both brows but didn't reply until he'd poured himself a cup of coffee and sat down again. 'This and that. I can't remember it all in detail.'

'Can't you? Then allow me to jog your memory, Mr O'Rourke. Do you recall Guy mentioning that we had a problem with one of the models for the Renshaw contract?'

He shrugged. 'I might.'

Her lips snapped together and she took a quick step towards him. 'And do you remember Guy asking you what line you were in?'

He took a sip of his coffee then carefully put the cup down before smiling at her. 'I do seem to recall something about it, yes.'

'Then you must *recall* what you told him?' Another couple of steps had her standing in front of his chair.

'Much the same as I told your friend Renshaw, I imagine. Why? What's the problem, sweetheart?'

'I am not and never will be your sweetheart! And the problem is that, thanks to what you apparently said, Guy has got it into his head that *you* would be the perfect choice to replace the model who's gone sick! I couldn't believe it when he told me this morning. I spent almost an hour trying to convince him that the idea was crazy and then ... then ...' She stopped abruptly, drawing in a long angry breath which did little to unlock the furious jumble of words.

'Then?' he prompted.

'And then this afternoon Damian arrived.' She sank down abruptly on to a chair and ran her hand wearily over her eyes. 'Damian is determined that Egypt, the new Renshaw fragrance which we are promoting, will be a huge success. He intends it to be *the* market leader this Christmas, the result of a massive promotion throughout the summer months. No expense is to be spared, and all photographic work is to be done on location in Egypt because he feels, quite rightly, that it would be impossible to duplicate the atmosphere in a studio. Now he has decided that he wants to come along on the shoot next week just to ensure that it all goes well!'

'And that presents a problem?'

'Yes! Of course it does!'

'So can I take it that his interest in you hasn't waned after last night?'

Natalie gave him a murderous look. 'No, it hasn't! If anything he's keener than ever, and it's all your fault, O'Rourke! If you hadn't ... hadn't *challenged* him last

night by trying to prove how much you knew then I'm
sure Damian would have turned his attention to someone
else. Now, after this afternoon's conversation, it's obvious that he's keener than ever to capture my heart because it would be such a blow to your over-inflated ego!
And accompanying us to Egypt seems to him the perfect
opportunity to do so!'

Flynn smiled lazily, studying Natalie's softly flushed
face in its frame of silky black curls. 'I don't think I'm
wholly to blame, honey. I think a large part of the blame
must rest squarely on your own shoulders.' His voice
had deepened to a husky warmth which played sudden
havoc with Natalie's already stretched nerves. 'You are
a beautiful woman. It's no wonder that Renshaw wants
you.'

'That has nothing whatsoever to do with it! If you
had handled last night with a bit more tact and diplomacy then I'm certain Damian would have found other
fish to fry!'

Flynn chuckled. 'What a metaphor! Still, I don't
suppose there's any point in arguing about it now. I
imagine that you didn't come here just to voice your
complaints. So what do you want, Natalie?'

'What I *want* is to turn back the clock twenty-four
hours so that I'd never left that message on Marcus's
phone!' Now that the moment had arrived when she had
to tell O'Rourke what she wanted him to do it seemed
the hardest thing in the world. She'd dealt with persistent admirers before, so surely she could handle
Damian Renshaw? Yet even while she tried to convince
herself she couldn't help but recall the expression on
Damian's face that afternoon when he'd informed her
of his plans. Shaking Damian off wouldn't be easy and

she couldn't afford to antagonise him when it could mean losing the account even at this late stage.

'But that's impossible, so...?' He glanced at his watch then looked back at her. 'I hate to hurry you but I am expecting someone.'

How did she just *know* it was a woman? Not that it should be any surprise because O'Rourke was anything but a monk and must attract women by the score. So why did Natalie feel her temper give a sudden little surge at the idea? It was very odd.

She glowered at him, black eyes sparkling with anger as they met the cool green ones. 'Excuse me! I wouldn't want to disrupt your social life any more than is strictly necessary.'

'You aren't. There's some business I need to sort out.' There was a faint edge to his voice, a sharpness to the look he gave her which piqued her curiosity.

'I thought you told Damian that you were on holiday?'

'I did, but that doesn't mean I can completely disregard any problems which arise and need my attention.'

'What exactly do you do? You said that you were a business associate of Marcus's so are you a lawyer too?' She studied him closely, watching the faintly ironic tilt to his lips when he replied.

'No, I'm afraid not.' He glanced at his watch again, making no attempt to disguise the action. It was a less than subtle hint that time was passing and that he wanted her to leave and Natalie realised she couldn't put off telling him why she'd come much longer, no matter how much she might long to.

'Last night, when you and Guy discussed the promotion, were you serious about being interested in working on it?'

He shrugged, watching her through half-closed eyes. 'I might have been.'

'But how would it fit in with your work if there are problems you need to deal with?'

'Oh, I think you can leave me to sort them out, Natalie. These things have a way of working themselves out all in good time.' There it was again, that faint edge to his voice, but before Natalie could start wondering about it again he continued, 'So what are you saying, Natalie? That you want me to accept the job as one of the models on this promotion?'

She nodded, feeling a sudden rush of nerves locking her throat. She'd run through all the pros and they outweighed the cons, but was she still making a huge mistake by letting O'Rourke get even further involved in her life?

'And if I do accept, you want me to continue with the role I played last night?' His voice dropped a note, deliberately seductive now, and she glared back at him.

'Yes! Believe me, if there had been any other way...! But you made such a good job of convincing Damian that you and I... Well, I'm sure you remember what happened as well as I do!'

'Of course. And I understand your predicament, Natalie. To suddenly produce another lover would do little for your reputation, wouldn't it? No woman likes to be thought of as someone who hops from one bed to another at the drop of a hat.'

'How perfectly you put things, O'Rourke! So how do you feel about the idea?'

'I'm always open to offers, honey, if the terms are right. So what exactly are you offering?'

That was better. She could handle this businesslike approach far easier than that suggestive hint of intimacy. Maybe the plan wasn't quite so risky after all.

'Well, for a start you'll get a free, all-expenses-paid trip to Egypt, staying in one of the best hotels. Then there will be your fee, which I can assure you will be generous.'

'Mmm. I see. What else?' His voice was a deep purr, like the rumble of a big cat lulling its prey into a false sense of security before it sprang. But, no matter how she tried, Natalie couldn't sense any danger now.

'Well, the photo session should only take a week to complete. After it's over then I'm sure I can stretch the budget so that you can stay on in Egypt for a while so that you can have that holiday you planned.'

'And you really imagine that Renshaw will agree to it, my taking over the role in the advertisement?' He sounded sceptical, not that Natalie could blame him after last night's less than friendly meeting between the two men. But she'd gone over it all and she was certain it would work out.

'Yes. Naturally Damian wouldn't agree to your being there just to keep me company, but if you have a legitimate reason then I'm sure it will work out. And after all,' she added pointedly, 'I can tell him with all honesty that it was Guy who suggested you for the role.'

'You seem to have it all thought out but...' He gave a slight shrug, his wide shoulders straining the thin cotton shirt as he smiled ruefully at her. Natalie bit her lip; she didn't want to ask the question but what choice did she have after all?

'But...what?' she asked as calmly as she could manage.

'But I've been to Egypt before, several times actually. I can't say that I'd been planning on going back again right at this moment when I've just spent the past couple of months out of the country.' He picked up his cooling coffee and sipped it slowly then set the cup down again.

'Surely the fee would be some compensation,' she retorted, a shade more sharply than perhaps she should have in the circumstances. After all, she was asking him to do her a favour yet she couldn't help feeling that he was playing with her.

'I don't really need the money, sweetheart. I earn more than enough, believe me.'

If he thought she was going to play mouse to his cat much longer he was sadly mistaken! 'Then what do you want, O'Rourke? From what Guy told me you were keen on the idea last night, so what's the matter today? Why don't you tell me what you're after and stop wasting our time?'

'Well, if you insist.' He smiled, his eyes sweeping over her in a look she could feel, his voice dropping to a husky level which stirred her senses. 'You've told me about the free trip, the generous fee, even the possibility of extending the holiday, but ultimately all those are coming from Renshaw. So what are *you* prepared to offer me, Natalie, as an extra little incentive?'

She had thought in her innocence that she'd covered it all, every single possible flaw. Yet the biggest flaw of all was sitting there right in front of her: six feet of gloriously handsome, unpredictably dangerous male. Exactly what sort of 'incentive' was Flynn O'Rourke expecting?

Natalie jumped to her feet and glared at him. 'Precisely what do you mean?'

He stood up too, coming close enough that she could feel the warmth of his body and smell the clean freshness of his skin. 'I'd have thought that was obvious. So tell me what kind of particularly juicy carrot you're prepared to dangle in front of me, Natalie, just to tempt me to help you out.'

Oh, if she were a man she would hit him! How dared he try to proposition her this way? But before she actually told him what she thought she would let him dig himself in a bit deeper. 'What sort of carrot would you like me to offer you, Flynn?' she asked softly as she stared seductively into his eyes and gave an inviting little smile. 'I imagine it all depends what you call an... incentive.'

He seemed to hesitate, possibly because he couldn't believe his luck that it was so simple! Then his sea-green eyes dropped deliberately to the full curve of her mouth and lingered there. 'A kiss.'

Disturbed by the sensations that that lingering look was arousing, Natalie took a moment to react to what he'd said. 'Pardon? A kiss? Is that what you really said?'

'Yes.' He smiled into her startled face, mockery dancing now in the depths of his eyes and curving the chiselled perfection of his lips. 'You seem shocked, Natalie. But why? What were you expecting me to ask for? Surely not what springs immediately to mind. Tut, tut, but you do me an injustice, sweet.'

'No one could do you that, O'Rourke! You must be the most scheming, conniving, low-down——' She broke off and swallowed a gulp of air so that she could continue. 'You really expect me to believe that a kiss is all you want from me?'

'Yes. You can even have it in writing if you want, a proper contract all signed and sealed.' He walked over to the desk and picked up a pen then handed her the sheet of paper. 'There you are—a guarantee that I won't make any other demands on you apart from one kiss. I'd call it a bargain really.'

Natalie studied the bold black letters, not quite able to believe that it was all he was asking for. But if he did suddenly decide to try to milk the situation then at least she had this to back her up.

She folded the paper and carefully slipped it into her bag then glanced over at him. 'All right, then, you have a deal. I accept the terms.' She dropped her bag on to the chair and walked towards him with an expression of resignation on her face which wasn't reflected by the tumultuous thumping of her heart. 'I suppose we may as well get it over with.'

Flynn held his hand up, smiling eloquently at her. 'Not yet. I didn't make that clear, did I? I shall take my "fee" when and where I decide. That's part of the deal.' He glanced around the immaculate room dismissively then looked back at Natalie. 'Here doesn't seem to be quite the place I had in mind.'

Natalie turned away without a word and picked up her bag, telling herself that it was ridiculous to feel alarmed. A kiss was a kiss no matter where it was taken or when. 'As you choose. I'll be in touch with you tomorrow. Naturally there are a few things which will need sorting out, not least of which is whether you're photogenic or not. I shall arrange for you to have a portfolio done and then we'll go from there.'

'Fine.' Flynn walked with her to the door but made no attempt to open it as he looked down at her with a faint lift of his brows. 'Have you ever been to Egypt before, Natalie?'

She shook her head, the long black curls dancing around her shoulders. A few strands caught on Flynn's white shirt but before she could free them he smoothed them into place, his fingers lingering for a heartbeat before his hand dropped to his side.

'It's an unforgettable experience even in these days of commercialism.'

Natalie's pulse was hopping up and down, reacting crazily to the intimacy of the gesture so that she sounded almost curt. 'I'm not going there to enjoy myself. I have a job to do.'

'Of course. But wait until you see the moonlight on the desert.' His gaze slid to her mouth and stayed there as he continued in a tone which made her burn with a sudden rush of heat along her veins, 'Up above the sky is black velvet, so deep and dark that it feels as though you could reach up and bury your hands in its folds, while down below the sands shimmer like silver dust. It will be a magical moment when you first see it, Natalie. I can guarantee that you won't forget it...ever.'

Natalie opened the door, forcing a strained goodbye from lips which felt feverishly hot. She summoned the lift, closing her eyes in relief as it slid down to the ground floor, and knew at once that that was a mistake. Suddenly all she could see in her mind's eye was the vivid picture Flynn had painted—that desert scene: the velvet sky, the silver sparkle of moonlight on the sand, and, in the centre of the picture, herself enfolded in Flynn O'Rourke's arms as he took his dues...and kissed her!

CHAPTER FOUR

CAIRO wasn't how Natalie had imagined. She stared out of the taxi, mesmerised by a skyline of soaring sky-scrapers interspersed with the graceful minarets of the many mosques.

'Not quite what you expected, Natalie?'

Her heart leapt at the sound of Flynn's voice. She turned to look at him, trying hard to dismiss the strange little shiver which ran disturbingly down her spine when he smiled at her. She had always compared other men to Marcus and invariably found them wanting, his dark good looks making them pale into insignificance. So why did her heartbeat quicken and her blood seem to flow a degree more warmly when she looked at Flynn now? It was very odd.

She pushed the question from her mind and kept her voice as level as she could. 'I guess not. I thought it would be like you see in films—all dusty bazaars and alleys with pedlars pushing their wares at you, not full of modern buildings.'

Flynn laughed deeply, stretching his long legs as best he could in the cluttered confines of the taxi. The party plus their luggage had been just too large to fit into the two taxis booked to collect them from the airport. Natalie had volunteered to stay behind and take the bulk of the heavy equipment with her and Flynn had immediately announced that he would stay with her. He had ignored her protests, calmly commandeering another vehicle and helping the driver stow the cases inside.

Natalie had been only too aware of the speculative looks being cast their way when Flynn had taken charge but there had been little she could do about it. She couldn't tell the others the truth and risk it getting back to Damian. She'd had to content herself with the thought that what she was doing was for everyone's benefit. This account would keep them all in jobs for some while to come!

'Oh, you'll see plenty of those. Beneath all that modern façade Cairo is little changed from how it has been for centuries. It must be one of the most fascinating cities in the world, but that's to be expected when you consider its history and the fact that it's been at the centre of trade between East and West for centuries.'

Despite herself, Natalie was intrigued. 'I never thought about that. You seem to know an awful lot about the city. Have you been here just for holidays or have you had business here?' she queried curiously.

He glanced away, his eyes faintly hooded as they focused on the passing scene. Natalie had the sudden feeling that he didn't want to discuss his previous visits to the city—but why? What was the mystery? Yet when he answered there was no hint of anything in his tone to back up her suspicions.

'A bit of both actually. But no matter how many times I've been here I'm still stirred by that sight.' He indicated a spot over Natalie's shoulder. She looked round, gasping as she saw the gigantic peaks of the three Pyramids of Giza rising in the distance. She'd seen photographs of them so many times that they'd become a tourist cliché, but nothing could detract from the sense of awe she felt on actually seeing them for the first time.

'I never dreamed they'd be so huge!' she admitted breathlessly.

'Wait until you stand at the base of the Great Pyramid.' Flynn turned his gaze back to Natalie, studying her rapt expression with a disturbingly intent light in his eyes. 'It's unforgettable by day but the best time to see it is at night. Then the magic really gets to work.'

Natalie felt her pulse skip wildly. It was the way Flynn was looking at her, those aqua eyes filled with a warmth which made her feel light-headed. But she had to remember why they were here!

She flicked another quick glance at the Pyramids then forced herself to smile coolly and not betray her inner turmoil. 'Don't get too carried away, O'Rourke. You're here to do a job. Is that clear?'

He rested his blond head back against the hard seat, his mouth quirking ruefully. 'As crystal. And part of that *job* entails my acting as your pretend lover, isn't that right, Natalie? By the way, you never did tell me how Renshaw took the news that I'm to be in the advert. Was he pleased?'

Natalie ground her teeth. O'Rourke made an art-form out of finding things to say to ruffle her. Pretend lover indeed! 'Damian doesn't know yet, as it happens. He had to fly to New York and he'll be coming on from there. However, I did clear it with Renshaw's marketing director. She was...happy enough.'

It was a blatant understatement but Natalie would be damned if she'd tell him how the elegant middle-aged woman had positively drooled when she'd shown her the pictures of O'Rourke! She had to admit that they had been remarkably good, even though he'd made no obvious effort to dress up when they'd been taken. Yet the casual shirt and jeans, the slightly mussed hair falling over his forehead, had made him look undeniably sexy!

'So it doesn't look as though there'll be any problems on that score. Good. You seem to have tied up all the loose ends, Natalie.'

All except one, and that had given her a few sleepless nights! 'More or less.'

'Is there something worrying you?' There was an edge to Flynn's voice as he asked the question, a sharpening of interest in his eyes as they rested on her, and Natalie looked away.

Of course there was something worrying her! Six feet of blond Adonis going by the name of Flynn O'Rourke, not to mention that kiss he intended to take as payment. Yet thumbscrews and boiling oil wouldn't have made her admit it!

'No! Everything's fine. Why shouldn't it be?' she snapped.

'So there's been no problem with Marcus?'

'Marcus? What do you mean?'

He eased himself more comfortably in the cramped space, smiling understandingly. 'Well, it occurred to me that he might not like the idea of you and me pulling off this stunt. Of course we know that it's all an act but some people might get the wrong idea. What did he say when you told him, or haven't you done so yet?'

'No, I haven't!' Natalie took a deep breath, running her hand through her hair, almost glad when her fingers tangled in the curls and tugged painfully on the roots because it steadied her. Once again, Flynn had touched a raw nerve, although she couldn't in all honesty believe that he knew he'd done so. It would be wonderful to think that Marcus *would* care but she wasn't foolish enough to hope for too much! Although once he got back and they had that promised talk then maybe things would change...

'Perhaps it was wiser to be discreet, Natalie.' Flynn gave a low laugh. 'Naturally I can appreciate that Marcus might be jealous at the thought of you and me heading off into the desert.'

The mocking words cut short her musings and she glared at him. 'Don't be ridiculous! Of course Marcus wouldn't be jealous! He...he knows he has no need to be,' she amended quickly when Flynn raised his brows at her vehemence.

She looked down, plucking nervously at the edge of her sweatshirt, afraid that she might have said too much already. Flynn obviously believed that she and Marcus had some sort of intimate relationship and she didn't want to disabuse him of that idea. It provided her with a barrier she could hide behind, yet why should she feel she needed its protection? It should be enough that she loved Marcus. She shouldn't need anything else to keep her safe from Flynn's undoubted charm!

'I understand,' he said smoothly.

Natalie shot him a wary glance and felt her temper surge at the expression on his face. 'I doubt that! The simple fact is that I haven't told Marcus because I haven't spoken to him since he went away.'

'Is it usual for him to go off like this without leaving word of where he is?'

The question made Natalie hesitate; it put into words the uneasy feeling she'd had since she'd found out that Marcus had gone off. 'Well, no. It is odd but...' She paused.

'But?' Flynn prodded.

'I don't know, but Marcus seems to have been acting strangely recently. I can't quite put my finger on what it is but there's been something...well, different about him.'

'Has there? And you're sure you have no idea what it is?'

Flynn's tone had sharpened and Natalie jumped as she shot him a startled look. 'No, I haven't. Anyway, I'm sure it's none of our business, although I'm certain Marcus would appreciate knowing how concerned you are about him, O'Rourke!'

'Oh, I'm always concerned if a friend has a problem, Natalie. Look how concerned I've been about helping you.' His voice was as smooth and rich as dark chocolate now. Natalie felt it slide through all her senses, stirring them to life, but she wasn't going to allow such foolishness to cloud her judgement.

'You can cut out the play-acting! I never wanted you to muscle your way into my life and if I had any choice then we wouldn't be here. But one thing you and I shall never be is friends!'

'I'm sure you're right.' He paused as though considering what she'd said then continued softly, 'If I'm honest then I must confess that friendship isn't what I have in mind.'

'Now look here, O'Rourke...'

He cut her off with a throaty laugh. 'Sorry, honey, but I find it almost irresistible not to tease you when you rise so beautifully to the bait.' He glanced out of the window as the taxi turned. 'Ah, looks as though we've arrived.'

Natalie gripped the strap of her bag. 'I suggest you confine yourself to necessities,' she snapped. 'And teasing or baiting me isn't on the list!'

She pushed the door open as the taxi stopped but Flynn caught her arm and prevented her from getting out.

'It is necessary to build up some sort of rapport between us, Natalie. You can't treat me as a business as-

sociate otherwise Renshaw will see through the act in no
time. Like it or not, you and I have to appear…intimate.'

He was right but did he have to put it that way? Her
blood quickened at the suggestive note in Flynn's deep
voice but she held back the ensuing flood of sensation.
'Leave me to worry about Damian! You just concentrate
on what you came here to do. I imagine you've quite
enough to keep you fully occupied!'

His fingers tightened as he bent towards her. 'Meaning
what, precisely?'

His voice was edged with something she didn't understand and the look he gave her was searching. It made
her feel strangely uncomfortable, as though Flynn was
looking for answers to questions which were important
to him.

Natalie shrugged, feigning indifference to hide her
unease and the strange ripples of sensation which were
still affecting her more than she wanted them to. Flynn
was interfering, pushy and arrogant; her head knew that
but her body seemed to be blind to such glaring faults!
'That making the advert will occupy a great deal of your
time, and that the rest of it you will be…'

'Playing the part of your lover?' He let his hand slide
down her arm, leaving a tingling sensation of warmth
behind when he finally removed it. 'Don't worry, Natalie,
I shall do my best to ensure that you are satisfied—on
both counts.'

His tone mocked her and Natalie felt her face colour.
Those warm aqua eyes hinted at things she wouldn't put
into words yet which sent sexual awareness rocketing
through her system. Flynn O'Rourke was a handsome,
sensual man, and everything feminine in her responded
to it even though she didn't want to! Loving Marcus
apparently didn't make her immune to his appeal.

She got out of the cab without another word, hauling cases after her, more disturbed than she cared to admit. In some indefinable way it made her feel that she was betraying Marcus, and she bitterly resented it. What she felt for Marcus was an integral part of her life, yet Flynn seemed to shake its very foundations. What was it about him which disturbed her so? She had the feeling that the answer to that wouldn't be simple. Nothing ever was around him!

'Leave that to me.' Flynn came around and calmly moved her aside before taking over the task of unloading the cases. He flicked her a quick glance. 'Why don't you go in and register? This won't take long.'

Natalie glared at his broad back as he bent back to the task. Who did he think he was, taking charge all the time? She half opened her mouth to berate him then closed it with a sigh. The last thing she needed right now was to start yet another of their convoluted arguments which she never seemed to win!

It was cool inside the hotel. Natalie made her way to the reception desk, admiring the magnificent oriental chandeliers which hung from the painted ceilings. Guy and his wife had stayed here on a recent sightseeing trip and it had been on his recommendation that Natalie had booked it for their base. They had been granted permission to use the hotel and its grounds for some of the photos, to provide a contrast to those to be taken in the desert. Now as she looked round she knew that it was absolutely perfect for...

Her satisfaction melted away as Flynn stepped through the doors and came striding confidently towards her. He had dressed casually that day, his grey trousers and cream sweater oddly echoing her own choice of taupe trousers and white sweatshirt. But even without the benefit of formal clothing the desk clerk sprang to attention, ignoring Natalie as he smiled courteously at O'Rourke.

'Yes, sir? May I be of assistance?'

'The name's O'Rourke. I imagine you received my telex?'

'Of course, sir, and all the arrangements have been made as you requested, Mr O'Rourke.'

'Good. I'll register, if you would like to attend to Miss Walters first?'

The clerk bowed, turning away to sort through some keys. Natalie glanced from him to Flynn and frowned. What was going on? She had made all the arrangements herself, so why had O'Rourke needed to contact the hotel?

'What's going on?' she demanded in a low voice.

'Going on?' Flynn signed the form with a flourish then replaced the pen before smiling quizzically at her. 'Sorry, but I don't know what you mean.'

Natalie caught his arm and drew him away from the desk. 'Come on! You're up to something and I want to know what it is. Why did you send a telex? What was it about?'

'You really do have a suspicious nature, Natalie.' He sighed when she continued to glare at him. 'There were one or two things I needed to sort out.'

'Things? To do with your business, do you mean?'

'Sort of. Nothing for you to worry about, though.' He sounded unperturbed, at ease, and just for a moment Natalie found herself hesitating. Was she making a mistake by suspecting him of some sort of chicanery?

She toyed with the idea for the whole of thirty seconds then dismissed it. Flynn was up to something; the question was what?

'Miss Walters?' The desk clerk claimed her attention and handed her a key as he called over one of the porters to take her bags. 'Ahmed will show you to your room, madam.'

Natalie accepted the ornate brass key and shot Flynn another assessing look but his face betrayed nothing apart from a vague puzzlement, as though he found her accusations hard to understand.

'This way, madam.' The porter bowed as he picked up her bags and led the way towards the lifts and Natalie had no option but to follow him. Yet as she stepped inside she couldn't help glancing back across the foyer at Flynn, who was still by the desk. Even as she watched he pulled out his wallet and withdrew several notes, handing them over to the young clerk. Then before Natalie could see anything more the lift started to move.

Still speculating on what was going on, Natalie followed the porter along the third-floor corridor only to come to an abrupt halt when he opened a door. 'Oh, but there must be some mistake. I didn't request a suite...'

'But I did.'

Flynn was suddenly there, taking her arm to lead her into the huge sitting-room as he glanced back at the porter. 'Take the bags through to the bedrooms, please.'

'Let me go, damn you!' Natalie wrenched her arm free, her face flaming as the porter shot them a startled look. She waited until he'd disappeared into one of the bedrooms then rounded on O'Rourke. 'I knew you were up to something! I just didn't get a chance to work out what. But if you imagine that I'm going to share this suite with you then think again!'

Flynn raised both brows as he swept a hand around the room. 'You really object to staying here?'

Natalie barely glanced around the elegant blue and gold sitting-room, unmoved by the opulent furnishings. 'I object to staying here...with *you*,' she snapped. 'Did you really imagine I would agree?' She laughed tauntingly. 'Your ego must be even bigger than I thought!'

'It has nothing whatsoever to do with my ego, Natalie.' He stopped as the porter reappeared, handing him a tip with the ease of one accustomed to dealing with such matters.

Natalie stared at the door as the man left, feeling the most absurd urge to flee after him. Flynn O'Rourke had a way of making things go the way he wanted! Her back stiffened, her chin tilting defiantly; he wasn't getting his way over this, though!

'What do you imagine Renshaw's plans are, Natalie?'

'I beg your pardon?' She started nervously, thrown by the unexpected question. Flynn sighed as he walked to the low couch and dropped down on to its blue and gold cushions, treating Natalie to a level look while he selected a fig from the basket on the table in front of it then continued in the same infuriatingly rational tone. 'Do you really imagine that he will just step aside once he knows I'm here?' He shook his head. 'No way. Our friend Damian will do his level best to take advantage of the fact that you and he are under the same roof. Sharing this suite with me will curtail any unwanted...nocturnal visits, shall we call them?'

'You don't honestly expect me to believe that Damian would *force* his attention on me?' she said sceptically.

'I'm saying that it is a possibility. The man is obviously keen. He wouldn't be going to such lengths as coming out here if he weren't. So think it through for yourself.' He took a bite out of the fig, strong white teeth cutting through the juicy flesh. It was a strangely sensuous experience watching him eat as he lounged there like some eastern potentate. All he needed was a harem of beautiful women and he'd be set. But if he imagined *she* was auditioning for that role he could think again!

'And how do I know it won't be a case of out of the frying-pan into the fire?' she demanded hotly.

Flynn laughed as he stood up and came over to her. 'Because you have my word.' He paused deliberately, fixing her with an unwavering stare that she couldn't seem to break. 'I promise that I won't use this situation to my advantage by seducing you . . . unless you want me to, that is.'

Natalie gasped in outrage. 'Never! Don't flatter yourself, O'Rourke. I shall never be that desperate!'

'Was that meant to be a challenge?' He tilted her chin so that she was forced to meet his eyes then smiled in a way which made a river of heat flow down her spine. 'It's a good job I'm enough of a gentleman to give you the benefit of the doubt.'

Natalie shook his hand off, hating the fact that her heart was thumping, her pulse popping like champagne bubbles. It was anger, that was all, nothing else, and definitely not that she wanted him to carry out that ridiculously chauvinistic threat!

'You haven't the first idea of what that means! A gentleman is someone who doesn't push his way in where he isn't wanted, someone who isn't so egotistical that he believes he is always right, someone who . . . who . . .' She paused then added triumphantly, 'Someone exactly like Marcus, in fact!'

Flynn's eyes were gleaming green shards of ice as they centred on her flushed face and stormy black eyes. 'Let's hope that Marcus continues to live up to your expectations, then. It would be a shame to see you disappointed by discovering that your idol has feet of clay.'

'What do you mean? Are you trying to tell me something...about Marcus?' Cold seeped through her whole body, stemming from the icy glaze in Flynn's eyes. Natalie had the sudden feeling that she was looking at a stranger, because he seemed so different now, his handsome face set and uncompromising, his whole body rigid with a tension and anger she didn't understand.

She took a shaky breath, deeply disturbed. 'What are you hinting at, Flynn?'

He seemed to collect himself, his face smoothing out, the tension easing from him so fast that Natalie wondered if her imagination had been playing tricks. He laughed gently. 'I'm not hinting at anything, honey. I just want you to see sense, that's all. It's a question of putting up with me or maybe suffering Renshaw's unwelcome attentions—that is if they really are unwelcome?'

Natalie bristled at his tone, which was little short of insulting now. 'And what do you mean by that?'

'Do I need to spell it out for you?' He smiled cynically when she arched an angry brow. 'Renshaw is rich and well-heeled, quite a catch, I believe. A lot of women would jump at what you're turning down. So perhaps you're having second thoughts, eh?'

Natalie's hand arced through the air but before it could connect with Flynn's cheek he'd caught her wrist and stopped her. Twisting her arm behind her back, he slammed her against his hard body so fast that she was left stunned by the impact then held her there while he stared coldly down into her widened eyes.

'Don't. It would be a big mistake. The last person who tried it ended up in hospital, and he outweighed

you by a good sixty pounds and had another six inches
of height to his advantage.' He let her go abruptly. 'It's
up to you what you decide to do. If you don't want to
stay here then I suggest you phone through to the desk
and make other arrangements.'

Natalie's hand shook as she reached for the telephone
without a word. She felt bitterly ashamed for having tried
to strike him but Flynn managed to make her more angry
than she'd realised she could be! She put through the
call but, after only the briefest conversation with the
clerk, hung up.

'Well?'

She started nervously at the harsh demand, avoiding
his eyes so that she wouldn't have to see that cold con-
tempt in their icy depths. 'It appears the hotel is full up.
Once they received your telex then they re-let my room.'

'Then there doesn't seem much you can do about it,
does there?' His voice was cold and unyielding, sending
shivers through her system. She shot him a wary look
then turned away when he smiled thinly at her. 'I suggest
you try remembering one pertinent fact about all this,
though, Natalie.'

'Which is?'

'That *you* are responsible for my being here. You asked
me to help you out.'

'Is that right?' She gave a shaky laugh which held scant
amusement. 'I wonder about that!'

'Meaning what precisely?'

'Meaning that if I stop to think then it seems to me
that I've had very little say in any of this!' She held her
hand up as she marked off points on her fingers. 'You
stepped in for Marcus and turned up at the opera; you
took me home and put me to bed, then while I was
sleeping off that migraine you convinced Guy that you

would be perfect for the advert. And now you've arranged for us to stay together in this suite!' Her face was troubled as she looked at him. 'I can't help feeling that I've been skilfully manoeuvred yet I don't understand why! So tell me just what you get out of all this, Flynn.'

Flynn laughed softly, stepping closer so that he could tilt her chin, his fingers smoothing along her jaw. 'Do I really need to answer that, my sweet? Which man wouldn't jump at the chance of helping out a beautiful woman like you?'

Natalie pushed his hand away and glared stormily at him. 'Don't give me that! It's just another line. Why won't you ever give a straight answer? It's the same when I try asking what you do for a living. You always pass it off!'

'I hadn't realised it was so important to you.' He gave a light shrug. 'It's no mystery, Natalie. I'm in the insurance business.'

'Insurance?'

Her dark eyes were full of doubts and he raised one brow in a mocking taunt. 'If you don't believe me then you can always ask Marcus. I'm sure he will verify that I'm telling the truth, although why I should want to lie about it is beyond me.' He picked up the telephone and offered it to her. 'Go ahead. Phone him. I shan't be the least bit offended.'

Natalie shook her head. 'You know I can't... I've no idea where Marcus is!'

'Of course not. Do you think he's left the country or what? He didn't give you any hint what his plans were?'

'No. I've already told you that!' There was a sharp edge to her voice that she couldn't hide. She felt keyed up enough by recent developments without these con-

stant reminders of how Marcus had gone away without
telling her where! 'Anyway, Marcus's whereabouts aren't
the problem!'

'But I am?' He raised both hands palm upwards in a
gesture of mock-defeat not reflected by the sparkle in
his eyes as they rested on her flushed face. 'Never mind,
Natalie. It's only for a week. I'm sure you'll survive.'

He turned and headed towards the bedrooms, closing
the door quietly behind him. Natalie stared at the closed
door, unable to shake off a deep feeling of unease. Every
time she and Flynn talked she ended up feeling that she
knew less about him rather than more. He was such a
mystery, a man who asked seemingly innocuous questions which left behind the feeling that they weren't half
so innocent as they seemed! He appeared to be unusually interested in Marcus's affairs yet she couldn't
understand the link between them.

She glanced at the telephone and sighed. If only she
could phone Marcus and speak to him then perhaps she
could make sense out of so much that was going on. It
would be good to hear his voice again, to put back into
her life the stability which seemed to be sadly lacking at
present. Ever since Flynn had turned up nothing had
been the same and it frightened her, as though her world
was being turned upside-down and she had lost all
control over it.

Life had been so straightforward not long ago. She'd
had her work and her dream that one day Marcus would
realise that he loved her. Now it was as though all that
had somehow become far less clear-cut. Even how she
felt about Marcus didn't seem quite so simple any longer.
Flynn aroused feelings inside her which both confused

and shocked her because they were feelings she *shouldn't* have about another man! Somehow she was going to have to work through what was happening but it wasn't going to be easy. Being around Flynn guaranteed that!

CHAPTER FIVE

'Do go on, Flynn. It's all so fascinating.' Zara laughed huskily as she leant across the table to touch Flynn's hand. 'I can't get over the number of places you've seen!' she added with wide-eyed wonderment.

Natalie picked up her glass of wine, wondering why she felt the sudden urge to toss its contents over the other woman. Flynn had entertained them all with a fund of witty anecdotes over dinner without appearing to dominate the conversation, and Zara had hung on to his every word in a way Natalie resented although she wouldn't try to work out why!

Flynn eased his hand away and picked up his glass, his green eyes holding a glint of amusement when they met Natalie's stormy ones. He quirked a brow in a silent, meaningful question as he took a sip of the wine and she looked away, her face flaming. She wasn't jealous! All right, so maybe he did manage to make her feel off-balance and, well, *unsettled*, but she'd had time to think about it now and the explanation was simple really; naturally she was on edge with the situation they were in and what they were trying to achieve while they were here, but jealous...never! It was the fact that he was in serious danger of ruining everything by not nipping the other woman's very obvious interest in the bud which annoyed her, nothing else!

She glanced round the rest of the party but they seemed to find nothing amiss. There were seven of them in all, including herself and Flynn: Zara, the other model for

73

the advertisement, Janette, the stylist who would be in charge of the sets, Gary who did hair and make-up, and David, the photographer, plus his assistant, Ben. And every single one of them was engrossed in O'Rourke's tale.

Flynn came to the end of the story and they all laughed. Natalie set down her glass and excused herself but, instead of heading for the powder-room, walked out into the lush gardens, needing a few minutes by herself.

Watching Flynn tonight as he had charmed them all had been oddly disturbing. It wasn't just annoyance over Zara and the damage it could cause which troubled her either. She'd felt as though she'd been watching someone playing a part. On the surface, Flynn appeared to be an amusing raconteur, a man of immense charisma who drew others to him, yet Natalie had the feeling that she was seeing only one side of the true picture. Yet what did she really know about O'Rourke? That charm he used to such effect to draw people to him also formed an impenetrable barrier beyond which she sensed few passed. There was a lot more to him than was at first apparent and suddenly she felt overwhelmed with a need to discover the real man, that tough, steely individual she'd caught only glimpses of so far.

'*Scusi, signorina.*'

Natalie jumped as a man pushed past her, forcing her off the path in his haste. She glared after him then started nervously when behind her Flynn suddenly spoke.

'Are you all right?'

'Apart from being nearly knocked over, yes. I don't know why he was in such an almighty rush. What's down there?' She stared after the man then glanced back at

Flynn and went cold at the expression she saw on his face before he smoothed it away with a dismissive shrug.

'Nothing, as far as I know. Still, perhaps it isn't wise to go wandering around at night by yourself like this.'

Natalie bristled at his high-handedness. 'I am perfectly capable of looking after myself, thank you. I don't need your advice!'

'Is that a fact?' He had her in his arms before she could breathe, pinning her against him.

'What do you think you're doing? Let me go!' Natalie demanded, pushing against his shoulders

'What I am doing, sweetheart, is proving to you that although you may think yourself capable of handling a situation the reality could prove far different.' He drew her closer, so close that she could feel every hard, lean inch of his body pressed against hers, feel the steely strength of the muscles beneath her hands. She pushed even harder, wanting suddenly to be free with a desperation which had its basis in nothing logical. Flynn wouldn't hurt her, she knew that and wasn't afraid for that reason, but there was no denying the sudden fear she felt at his being so close.

'Flynn O'Rourke, if you don't let me go this very instant then I...I...'

'You'll do what?' He moved his hand from her back to cup her cheek and force her to meet his gaze. Natalie renewed her struggles to break free but even though he was only using one arm to hold her now was unable to break his grip.

She glared up at him, hating her own weakness and hating him even more for all the odd breath-stealing sensations, rippling in hot waves through her body, which made a mockery of what she'd tried so hard to convince herself of. What she was feeling right now owed absol-

utely nothing whatsoever to their situation but everything to the fact that Flynn was holding her so close!

'I'll think of something, trust me! Now let me go.
You've had your fun, so enough!'

He shook his head, his face suddenly very grave, no
trace of amusement in the firm set of his mouth. 'It isn't
fun to prove to you how vulnerable you are, Natalie.
That isn't why I'm doing this. I just want you to be
aware that you must always be on your guard and never
place yourself in a situation which could prove more than
you can handle.'

'I was perfectly fine until you showed up!' She took
a firm grip on his shoulders and pushed with all her
might but Flynn easily retained his hold on her. Natalie
held her breath as she tried to summon up patience, but
patience and Flynn O'Rourke didn't go together. 'Look,
Flynn, it might give you some sort of macho pleasure
to prove your superior strength but it leaves me cold!'
She glared at him. 'Why don't you save it for Zara? I'm
sure she would be ecstatic to be on the receiving end of
such a show of masculine prowess!'

He laughed deeply, tilting her face towards the light
from one of the lamps which were strung along the path
at intervals. 'No, definitely not green. For a moment
there you had me worried, sweetheart.' His thumb
stroked the soft underside of her jaw, his voice dropping
to a soft, rich vibrancy which made a shudder of sensation uncurl in her stomach. 'There's no need for you
to feel jealous of Zara or anyone else. I'm all yours on
this trip, Natalie...every bit of me.'

'Jealous? Why, you...you egotistical...!' Words failed
her so she could only stand and glare her denial of the
charge, but he seemed unperturbed by her anger. He

looked past her, his eyes narrowing as he stared along the path.

'Did you know that man?'

Natalie looked round, startled by the sudden question. 'No. I've never seen him before. Why?'

Flynn shrugged but there was a steely glimmer in his green eyes as they returned to her face. 'No reason. But don't go wandering around by yourself again.'

'Your concern is touching. However, apart from you, I don't think there are too many bogymen lurking behind the bushes!'

'Oh, I wasn't lurking, Natalie. I followed you out here.' The chill eased from his expression, his eyes gleaming with a warmth which made her go hot all over as they centred on her parted lips. 'I must say that I'm glad I did now.'

'You are?' Her voice sounded husky, strained, revealing far more than she cared to about how she felt right then. Her fingers curled against the smooth cloth of his suit but with him holding her so close there was no place to move them to. 'I...I think you should let me go now, Flynn. You've proved your point.'

'Have I?' His voice seemed to have deepened, soft and disturbing as it carried through the quiet little night-time sounds of leaves rustling, a bird calling gently in some nocturnal burst of sound. It seeped through Natalie's body and set off a chain of reactions—first a tiny shiver, next a ripple, then a slow steady surge of tingles which ran along every nerve. Natalie had never felt so achingly conscious of every cell before, never felt this crazy sensation of coming to life bit by bit. It shocked her into stillness and kept her unmoving in the circle of Flynn's arms.

'I'd say there was still a lot to prove, Natalie, to you and to me.' There was an inflexion in those deep tones that she didn't understand yet couldn't query as his hand started a slow journey down her spine, his fingers tracing its length through the thin silk of her top. His hand moved again, sweeping up this time, not down, to curl around the delicate bones of her shoulder and run along to come to rest against the pulse at the base of her throat which was tapping out a message she could only guess at. Deep inside a small voice was trying to warn her that it was madness to stand here like this, but the sound of his voice seemed to have cast a spell over her which was growing stronger with each slow caress. With the last vestige of sanity she possessed, Natalie murmured an objection.

'Don't, Flynn. You mustn't.'

His laughter was quick and fierce, his hand moving up to cup her cheek while he stroked the smooth flesh with the pad of his thumb, lazy circles which made the heat inside her spread. 'I can't help it, Natalie. The man isn't born who could hold you in his arms and not want to touch you.' He bent closer, holding her gaze as he added softly, 'Or kiss you.'

Natalie's heart went wild, sending the blood surging along her veins. There were just inches between her and Flynn now, his breath warm and sweet on her parted lips, a precursor to the kiss they were about to share.

Natalie closed her eyes as she tried to summon up the strength to tell him to stop, but that seemed impossible to do—to fight not just him but her own desires as well. She wanted him to kiss her, wanted to feel the hard demand of his lips on hers, with a need which defied logic. He angered her more than any man had ever done, infuriated her with his arrogance and high-handed assurance, but she wanted him to kiss her!

'Flynn.' His name was a whisper which barely disturbed the night but she knew he'd heard it. Under her hands she felt his muscles tense, heard the small, sharp intake of breath just a moment before his mouth touched hers so lightly that it was more an impression than anything else, just a tantalising hint of what was to come. Yet before Flynn could deepen the kiss as Natalie longed for him to do someone spoke.

'Oh, sorry! I didn't mean to interrupt.'

The aching sense of disappointment was so strong that Natalie could have wept, yet Flynn just calmly stepped away from her, a rueful smile on his face. 'Don't worry, Zara. I'm sure Natalie and I will find plenty of other opportunities to carry on with what we were doing. Did you want us?'

Zara laughed, although there was a forced note to the sound. 'We've decided to go to the *son et lumière* show at the Sphinx tonight. Would you... and Natalie, of course... like to come?'

'Why not? You would like to see it, wouldn't you, darling?'

Natalie nodded, afraid to speak in case Flynn heard the anguish in her voice. There was no point in telling herself that what had happened couldn't have been more opportune; it must have convinced Zara that she and Flynn were a couple better than any hints could have done. She still felt wretched.

In near silence she let him escort her back to the group, responding automatically to the conversation throughout the remainder of the evening. Yet when she lay in bed that night she could recall little of what had been said and even less of what they had seen. She stared up at

the ornate ceiling with eyes which burned with unshed
tears of self-disgust. What kind of a woman was she
that she could act that way? She loved Marcus, yet
Marcus had been the last person in her thoughts in the
garden before. Flynn had seduced her with a few soft
words, an expert touch and she had been putty in his
hands.

Her love for Marcus should have made her immune
to the desire that Flynn had aroused in her, but she
couldn't lie to herself. She had wanted Flynn to kiss her,
wanted even more than that, if she was being completely
honest; but why? Why should she feel this way about
him? Why should all thoughts of Marcus fade so completely when Flynn held her in his arms? Was her love
not strong enough to withstand the test of another man's
attractions?

It was an oddly bitter thought yet not as bitter as the
realisation that it had meant less than nothing to Flynn.
He had shown no sign of regret when Zara had inter-
rupted them. It had been merely a game to him, a way
to prove that Natalie was as susceptible as any other
woman to his charms. But she would never let him use
her like that again!

A door suddenly closed softly, then quiet footsteps
crossed the sitting-room floor followed by the clink of
glass. Natalie frowned as she tried to ignore the small
sounds of movement in the sitting-room, but it was impossible. She could just imagine that damnable man,
O'Rourke, in the other room, pouring himself a drink
before sprawling comfortably on the couch. He would
have taken his jacket off and loosened his tie and most
probably rolled his shirt-sleeves up as he seemed to make
a habit of doing.

Music flowed through the closed door, not loud enough to wake her if she'd been asleep but Natalie hadn't managed to achieve that state yet. She burrowed her head into the pillows to block out the irritating little noises but she *heard* when Flynn put the glass down, *guessed* that the soft double thud was him kicking off his shoes, *knew* the very moment when he rested his head back on the cushions.

She rolled over and moaned quietly with sudden cold dread. Beyond that door was a man who had shown her tonight just how susceptible she was to his particular brand of charm. Would loving Marcus be enough to stop her being so vulnerable again in the future, now that she knew the effect Flynn could have on her? She hoped so. Flynn O'Rourke was a lot of things, from amusing to irritating, with so many shades in between. But to Natalie there was just one word to sum him up: *dangerous* . . . to her peace of mind!

'There's nothing more we can do, Natalie. We'll have to leave it for now and try again tomorrow.' David shrugged philosophically as he picked up the heavy metal camera case. 'It's just the way it goes sometimes.'

Calling to Ben to bring the rest of the equipment, he started back to the bus with the others trailing after him. Natalie watched them go, fighting to keep a rein on her temper. It had been one delay after another since they'd started out that morning, from the bus arriving late to take them out to the Sphinx where the first shots were to be taken, to the officials in charge of the site refusing to allow them to do so despite the fact that they had written permission. To Natalie's annoyance it had taken Flynn's intervention, and the handing over of various sums of money, to sort it out. And now, when they were finally ready to start, the whole area was teeming with people, making it impossible to get the shots they wanted.

'It might be better if you found a different location. One which isn't quite so popular.'

Natalie picked up her tote-bag and clipboard, sparing Flynn a chilly look. 'Thank you, but I'm sure we can work this out without any advice from you.'

'I was merely trying to be helpful. You do seem to be rather touchy today, Natalie. Is there something wrong?'

'Nothing that getting this . . . this *fiasco* over and done with won't solve!'

'I see.' His tone was smooth as silk yet Natalie felt colour sweep up her cheeks. She turned away, not wanting him to guess the cause of her irritation. She'd barely slept all night long and when she had her dreams had been filled with images and scenes she didn't want to recall in the clear light of day! Suffice it to say that Flynn O'Rourke had featured prominently in all of them!

She strode back towards the bus, screwing her eyes up against the glare from the sun while she tried to ignore the man at her side, but, as she knew from experience, that was impossible. No matter how hard she tried, she found herself glancing his way, her traitorous senses stirring at the sight he made in the flowing white robes he was wearing over loose white trousers and a white shirt which laced up the front. He had removed the head-dress and his blond hair was blown straight back from his forehead by the breeze, leaving the purity of his profile starkly unadorned. He looked magnificent as he strode along with the robes billowing around his tall, lean frame. The outfit was the one Natalie had designed for the part he was playing in the advertisement but he wore it with an easy assurance that few men could have matched. He reminded her of a chameleon, able to change one skin for another yet still appear completely comfortable. It just served to highlight once again how little she knew about him.

'I'll get out of these clothes and see you on the bus.'

He disappeared towards the rear of the vehicle where a small tent had been set up for their use. Natalie watched him go then shrugged off her momentary unease. She was allowing her imagination to run away with her. Flynn O'Rourke was an associate of Marcus's, a businessman who dealt in a highly respectable field. What more was there to know?

The hotel was quiet when they arrived back. David swept a glance around the deserted foyer then turned to Natalie. 'How about taking some of the indoor shots? I doubt we'll get a better opportunity.'

Natalie nodded. 'Yes, good idea. I'll just go and clear it with the manager then fetch my notes from upstairs. We can run through the scene while we have coffee.'

'Sounds great to me.' David sketched her a wave then headed briskly towards the coffee-lounge with the others hard on his heels—all except Flynn, that was.

Natalie shot him an exasperated look as she started towards the desk. 'Aren't you going along with them?'

He smiled broadly. 'If I were a sensitive sort of person then I would start to think you were trying to get rid of me, sweet.'

'You can save the endearments!' she snapped back. 'The audience has gone. And if you would like the truth then yes, I can't think of anything I would like more than being rid of you!'

'But unfortunately that isn't an option right now. Not with Damian winging his way here probably at this very moment. You will just have to make the best of a bad lot, I guess. I must say, though, Natalie, I do wonder if

you are always this sweet-natured? Does Marcus ever
find himself on the receiving end, or is it just me who
brings out this side of your nature?'

Natalie glared at him, hands resting on her slim hips.
'Do I really need to answer that?' She gave a mocking
little shrug. 'Still, you only have yourself to blame. If
you hadn't responded to my cry for help that night then
you and I would never have met.'

'Think so?' He moved closer, staring intently into her
angry eyes. 'I think our meeting was pre-ordained,
Natalie. Even if you hadn't made that call we would
have met some time.'

'I don't see why.' She fought the urge to move away,
all too conscious of his closeness, the intensity of that
sea-green gaze which seemed to see right inside her mind.

'Surely you've met other business associates of
Marcus's? I imagine it was only a matter of time before
our paths crossed.'

She didn't know whether to feel relieved or furious
when she heard his reply! His eyes had seemed to hold
a different message just now, another, far more disturbing reason for why they should have met... She
closed her mind to that thought, suddenly conscious of
how dangerous this shift in the conversation might prove
to be. She didn't want to confess that she'd met nobody
from that side of Marcus's life because it would say so
much about their relationship—far too much, in fact!
'Maybe.'

'I bet if we delved into it you and I would know quite
a few of the same people.' Flynn ran a hand through his
hair, casually brushing the heavy wave back from his
forehead. 'I know Marcus has been caught up in something complicated recently. It has links with a case going

to court in Italy soon. Perhaps he's mentioned it or the
people involved?'

'No. I don't recall anything about it.' She frowned.
'But what I can't understand is how your two paths cross.
There doesn't seem to be any obvious link between law
and insurance.'

'Oh, you'd be surprised, Natalie. Marcus and I have
done business together on many occasions.' There seemed
to be an edge to his voice which Natalie couldn't understand. However, before she could question him, the clerk
appeared, smiling broadly as he greeted Flynn. He
hurried away when Flynn enquired if there had been any
messages for him, coming back almost immediately with
a folded slip of paper which he handed over the counter
with a small bow.

Flynn made no attempt to read it as he glanced at
Natalie. 'I'll see you later, then, in the coffee-lounge.'

He was gone before she could think of anything to
say, leaving her aching with curiosity to know what was
in the message until she told herself sternly that it was
none of her business.

After gaining permission from the manager to start
the photo session, Natalie headed up to the suite, men-
tally going over what they would be trying to achieve.
The campaign was to be split into three sections and run
over succeeding months in all the glossy magazines. First
would come the desert photograph showing Zara
dreaming of the mystery man in white, then one taken
in the hotel's grounds when there would be just a tantalising glimpse of the man in the background. It was
only in the final one to be shot today in the hotel itself
that he would be seen, and only then that the name Egypt
would be revealed.

Natalie was gambling on the fact that the public would be so intrigued by that stage they would remember the advert and the product far better than one which merely blazed its name across each page.

Now, eager to get started, she unlocked the door, then screamed as a figure came hurtling towards her. It all happened so fast as the man rushed across the room and pushed her aside to race out of the door. Natalie reeled against the wall, her heart pounding with fright so that it took several minutes before she felt able to pick up the phone to call down to the desk.

'Natalie, David said to... What's wrong?'

Flynn suddenly appeared, his eyes narrowing dangerously as he took in her white face, the shaking hands clutching the receiver. In two long strides he was across the room, his hands firm and wonderfully reassuring as they fastened around her shoulders and eased her down on to the couch and he told her in a tone which brooked no argument, 'Tell me what happened.'

'There was a man...here...in the room when I opened the door. He...' She took a gulping breath, feeling Flynn's hands tightening.

'Did he hurt you? Natalie!' He shook her lightly, his eyes burning with anger as they focused on her pale face, yet she knew instinctively that it wasn't aimed at her.

'No. He just pushed me to one side as he ran out. It gave me a shock but I'm not hurt, really.'

Flynn let her go abruptly, his face set into grim lines which made a shiver run down her spine. Gone was the smooth, urbane charm now, to be replaced by something quite unfamiliar yet which she sensed was still an integral part of him.

'Well, that's something at least,' he said grimly. He crossed the sitting-room, flinging doors open to check the other rooms, then came back and leant against the sideboard as he watched Natalie closely.

'Did you recognise him? Can you describe him?'

She shook her head, her hands clasped to stop them from shaking. The intruder had frightened her yet she felt equally disturbed at witnessing Flynn's reaction. 'It all happened so fast that I never got chance to see him properly. He was just a blur.' She swept her hair back from her face then glanced at the phone which was half off its rest. 'I was about to phone the desk and get them to call the police when you arrived. I'd better do it now.'

'No.' Flynn stepped forward and took the receiver from her to set it back in place. 'It doesn't look as though anything has been taken. You probably disturbed him before he could find anything worth stealing. There isn't any point in calling the police.'

'But we can't just let him get away! All right, so perhaps nothing has been taken, although I haven't checked yet, but surely the fact that he was in here is enough!'

Flynn shrugged, folding his arms across his chest as he resumed his position against the sideboard. He looked almost indolent if one didn't look too closely, but Natalie's senses had been heightened by the incident and she could almost feel the tension emanating from him even though she couldn't fully understand it.

'Why don't you want me to contact the police, Flynn?' she asked quietly, studying him.

He shrugged. 'It isn't a question of what I want, Natalie, but what makes sense. Obviously it's up to you but I should warn you that involving the police will mean no end of delays. By the time you make a statement and all the paperwork is completed you could end up spending the next couple of days down at the station.'

'A couple of days?' She couldn't conceal her horror. 'You have to be joking?' She stared at him in disbelief but he shook his head with a regretful smile.

'I wish I were. But I know how things work in this country. This morning was the perfect example. We had all the permits signed but...' He paused eloquently. 'The police are very thorough but they work at their own speed and nothing can hurry them. As I said, it's up to you, but can you afford to get tied up at the police station for that long?'

Natalie bit her lip as she looked round the room. Nothing did appear to have been stolen and the last thing she wanted was more delays. She turned back to Flynn with a resigned shrug. 'I suppose you're right. I can't afford to lose all that time. Assuming nothing is missing then I'll take your advice and let it lie.'

'It's the wisest thing to do, Natalie. Why don't you go and check your room to set your mind at rest? But I doubt if you'll find anything missing.'

Natalie nodded. She got up and headed to her room then paused to glance back, the question she'd been about to ask Flynn about whether or not they should tell the others dying on her lips. He was standing in the middle of the room, staring down at the message slip he'd collected earlier, an expression on his face which filled her with sudden fear.

She turned away without uttering a word, closing the door behind her, unable to explain why she felt so scared. Flynn had looked so different just then, hard and tough and ruthless, a world away from the man she knew, and once again all the uncertainties surfaced.

Was he what he claimed to be or was he hiding some sort of a secret? Suddenly the need to find out once and for all what he was up to was overwhelming, although the reasons behind it weren't so clear. She had a deep feeling that there was some link to Marcus and naturally she wanted to know what it was in case it posed a threat to him. Yet at the back of her mind was another reason, one she didn't want to examine too closely. After all, why should she *care* what Flynn was involved in? And why should she pray that it wasn't anything too dreadful? Flynn O'Rourke meant nothing to her... did he?

CHAPTER SIX

'A TOAST . . . to a successful afternoon after a frustrating morning.' Flynn raised his glass, smiling around the group gathered in the bar. He took a drink of the wine then set his glass down and settled back in the chair, listening quietly as the conversation flowed around him.

Natalie sipped her own drink and studied him surreptitiously. Oh, he'd been just as entertaining over dinner but she'd sensed a certain watchful tension about him, an echo of what she'd witnessed earlier. Time after time his aqua eyes had swept the dining-room as though he was searching for someone, but who? All she knew was that the mask of charm he wore so well had never seemed so false as it did to her tonight.

'You're very quiet tonight, Natalie. What are you thinking about?'

She jumped guiltily when he spoke so that a few drops of wine spilled over the rim of her glass. Setting it down, she licked the droplets off her fingers then felt heat suffuse her when she looked up and found Flynn watching her, his eyes locked to the pink tip of her tongue. He raised his head, a flame burning in his eyes which sent fire scorching through her veins. Seconds seemed to melt into minutes under the heat of his gaze then Janette leant across the table to speak to them and broke the spell.

'So, how about you two? Do you fancy it or not?'

Natalie shuddered, letting out the breath she hadn't even known she was holding as she turned to the other woman with a forced smile. 'Sorry, what was that?'

Janette laughed good-naturedly. 'Mmm, you two did seem to be in a world of your own! Gary was just saying that there's a nightclub in the hotel grounds and we were debating whether or not to go.'

Natalie shrugged. 'As long as you remember that it's a five a.m. start in the morning.'

There was a general groan and a lot of grumbling but they were all professionals. Natalie had worked with all of them before and knew they all understood that the job came first. When it was finally decided that they would visit the club just for an hour or so, she opted to go along, preferring to stay with the group rather than be on her own to brood.

It had been so odd, what had happened just now, that strange feeling that time had stood still. She couldn't recall anything like it ever happening before and didn't want it to do so again because it scared her, made her feel as though things were slipping out of her control.

She stood up to follow the others but got no further than a couple of steps before Flynn stopped her, his fingers cool against her heated flesh through the sleeve of her red linen dress. 'I'll be along shortly. I need to make a phone call. Just make sure that you stay close to the others and don't wander off on your own.'

'I'm touched by your concern but I'm sure there's no need to worry about me.' Natalie arched a brow, feigning amusement to hide her sudden nervousness at his touch, the disturbing sensations it aroused. How many times had Marcus touched her this way, a light, friendly gesture meant to attract her attention? Yet she couldn't recall ever feeling this instant awareness, these *frissons* of re-

action rippling along every nerve! Yet it shocked her that
she should even make the comparison. Marcus was the
man she loved, so why did she feel the sudden need to
shout that aloud and keep on shouting it? To convince
Flynn that her interest lay elsewhere or to remind herself
of something she shouldn't need reminding of? What
role did Flynn have in her life apart from the obvious
one he was playing while he was here? What role did she
want him to have? was an equally disturbing question.

He returned her gaze quietly, no mockery in his eyes
as they held hers. 'We can't always anticipate everything
that happens in our lives, Natalie. No matter how hard
we try.'

There was a note in his deep voice which made her
heart beat heavily in sudden fear, as though with that
brief statement Flynn had stepped across the barrier she'd
tried so hard to erect between them. For a long tense
moment Natalie returned his gaze, all her uncertainties
glittering in the darkened depths of her eyes, then turned
away without a word and almost ran after the others.
Yet when she reached the glass doors which led out to
the gardens she couldn't help herself looking back,
wanting to prove to herself that she had imagined what
had flowed between them, that sudden feeling that they
were standing on the verge of something earth-shattering.

Her eyes followed Flynn as he made his way across
the lobby towards the door and she frowned. He had
definitely said that he had to make a telephone call, so
what was he doing going outside instead of returning to
the suite or even using the telephone at the reception
desk?

Drawn by a sudden need to find out, she followed
him. It was dark outside and Flynn had several yards'
start on her. Natalie hurried down the drive, keeping to

the shadows to lessen the risk of him spotting her if he looked back. Reaching a side-path which led to a part of the gardens she'd never explored before, he turned down it, his long legs eating up the ground as he quickened his pace. He seemed to be in a hurry—there was an urgency about his movements which intensified her curiosity. No way was Flynn out for a gentle evening stroll, so what was he up to? Did it have anything to do with the growing feeling she'd had that there was something going on? Would following Flynn now uncover some answers, and would they be ones she'd want to know? To discover that Flynn was mixed up in something unsavoury was an oddly painful thought.

Natalie slowed to an uncertain halt, staring after him as he disappeared into the shadows, feeling sick at the idea of what she might uncover, until her resolve hardened. Far better to find out than keep on wondering . . .

She never saw the man who stepped from the shadow of the trees which lined the path, had no warning as a hand clamped across her nose and mouth, the strong-smelling cloth it held stealing her breath at once. She struggled frantically, clawing at the cloth, but it was impossible to drag it away from her face. She slid into unconsciousness with a name on her lips which she'd had no chance to utter aloud.

Consciousness returned, bringing with it the name which had followed her down. 'Flynn!'

Natalie lay still, listening to the rasping echo of her voice, but there was no reply, no sound at all. Her head felt heavy, her mouth dry and sour with the lingering effects of the drug. She took a deep breath then forced herself to sit up and look around, but what she saw wasn't reassuring. Apart from the iron-framed bed she

was lying on and a battered chest holding an oil-lamp
beneath a boarded-up window, the room was bare.
Where was she? And who had brought her here?

Swinging her legs off the bed, Natalie struggled to the
door and tried the handle, but it was locked, as she'd
known deep down it would be. Now there was no reason
to cling to the hope that it had been some sort of awful
mistake. Someone had drugged her deliberately then
brought her here and locked her in!

Panic rose swiftly, finding a release as she pounded
against the thick wood. 'Let me out! Let...me...out!'

When the door was suddenly opened Natalie backed
away, her eyes filled with fear as she watched the man
come into the room. There was something vaguely familiar about him but she couldn't work out what with the
drug still lingering in her head.

'I see you are awake at last, *signorina*. Good. But
shouting like that will achieve little, believe me. There
is no one here to hear you apart from me.'

Natalie backed away from him as she tried to draw
the elusive memory to the forefront of her mind, but it
refused to come. 'Why have you brought me here?' she
demanded hoarsely. 'Who are you?'

He smiled coldly. 'Who I am does not matter,
Signorina Walters. As for why you are here...' He gave
a very Latin shrug. 'The details do not matter also. It
is enough to say that if your friend, Signor O'Rourke,
is prepared to be sensible then your stay will be short
and, hopefully, not too unpleasant.'

'Flynn? This has something to do with him?' Natalie
ran a hand over her throbbing temples, unable to hide
her shock. 'I don't understand.'

'We are not unreasonable people, *signorina*. We are
prepared to...how do you say?...to make the fair trade.

You in exchange for what we want. We shall all have to hope that Signor O'Rourke is eager to have you safely back with him, eh?'

He locked the door behind him as he left. Natalie went and sank down on the bed, feeling sick as all her previous suspicions were proved to be well-founded. This was all linked to Flynn! But what could he possibly have that was so valuable that these people were prepared to drug and abduct her to get it?

She went back over everything she knew, but it was so little and none of it equated with Flynn's claim to work in insurance or his links to Marcus... She gasped, struck by a sudden dreadful thought. What if those links were of a criminal nature and Flynn was someone Marcus had defended...for committing some sort of crime? Dear God!

It all started to make a crazy kind of sense: Flynn's initial reluctance to discuss his work, the growing feeling she'd had that he was hiding something which had made her follow him tonight, even... Here Natalie had to stop and take a breath to steady herself. *Even* the fact that Flynn had stopped her from calling the police after that intruder had been in their rooms! Just what was he involved in?

The question plagued her as the hours passed. Several times the man came to bring her food or to escort her to the small, dirty bathroom but he never said anything further and cut short Natalie's attempts to question him. Through the cracks in the window boards, Natalie watched the sun gain its zenith then start to slide from the sky and knew that a full day must have passed. What was going to happen next? Would they have contacted Flynn by now and laid down the terms of the exchange?

Would he agree? She couldn't bear to dwell on what might happen if he didn't!

She must have fallen into an exhausted doze when the sounds of shouting from the next room woke her. Natalie leapt off the bed and ran to the door, pounding on it with her fists. 'Let me out of here! Do you hear me? Let me out!'

'I imagine a dead man could hear you, sweet. Do you really need to scream like that?'

There was no mistaking the voice yet it sat oddly with the figure who suddenly appeared as the door was thrust open. Natalie backed away, her eyes enormous as they swept over the white-robed figure with the dark hair and eyes who stood smiling at her in a very familiar way.

'Don't you recognise me, Natalie? I'm cut to the quick.'

'Flynn?' Her voice sounded dry as dust, echoing with disbelief. 'Is . . . is that really you?'

'It is. Amazing the difference a drop of hair dye and some contact lenses can make.' He shot a look over his shoulder, his face suddenly sobering when he turned back to Natalie. 'Still, there's no time to go into that now. Come along.'

'Where? Where are you taking me? What's going on, Flynn? Tell me, damn you!' Perhaps it wasn't the most logical moment to start demanding answers but as reaction set in Natalie couldn't help herself.

'That wasn't a request, honey, it was an order. Save the histrionics until later when we've more time to deal with them.'

He had her by the arm and through the door before Natalie could stop him. She tried to wriggle free, twisting and squirming in his grasp, then stopped abruptly as she caught sight of the figure slumped on the floor by the table.

'Is...is he dead?' she whispered in a horrified tone.

Flynn didn't bother sparing the man a glance. 'No. But I imagine he'll have a headache to beat all others when he comes round. Now let's get out of here before any of his cronies turn up. I hate to ruin my image but I doubt I'd be a match for more than one at a time.'

He wrenched the door open, then shot a quick glance outside before hauling her after him, half dragging and half carrying her to a battered Jeep which was parked out of sight down an alley next to the ramshackle house. He helped her inside then slid behind the wheel, starting the engine and pulling away in a cloud of dust.

Natalie took a long, shaky breath, feeling the ripples of shock coursing through her body when she glanced back at the house as they skimmed over the rough road. 'I want to know what's been going on. I think I deserve some sort of explanation!'

Flynn kept his eyes centred on the road, increasing his speed as they left the village behind. 'Unfortunately, you got involved in something you shouldn't have. I apologise.'

'You apologise?' She rounded on him in sudden fury, eyes glittering fiercely. 'I was drugged and abducted and you think that saying *sorry* is going to make up for it?'

'No, but there isn't anything else I can say right now.' He cut her an icy stare, his hands moving skilfully on the wheel as he turned the Jeep on to a track which had the vehicle lurching from side to side as they sped along it.

'You could try explaining what you're involved in! That man back there told me that I had been kidnapped because you have something he and his friends want. I want to know what it is. I want to know what you're involved in, Flynn!'

'It's better that you don't know, Natalie. It will serve no purpose telling you. For your own good I suggest that you leave me to handle it the way I see fit.'

She smiled cuttingly, her temper fuelled by echoes of the fear she'd lived with for the past few hours. What would have happened if Flynn hadn't found her . . .? She blanked out the thought, feeding her anger because it was all she had left between her and a total loss of control. 'For my own good, eh? I wonder why that phrase is usually used to excuse something unpleasant, like eating your spinach or taking cod-liver oil?'

He laughed suddenly, a low roll of sound which made her toes curl despite her fury. 'I don't recall ever being likened to cod-liver oil before.'

'I'm sure you haven't! I'm sure most people are taken in by the famous O'Rourke charm, that wonderful face you present to the world! But even without this little episode to back up my suspicions I was beginning to wonder if it wasn't all just a marvellous front, that the real Flynn O'Rourke wasn't someone completely different!'

'How perceptive of you, Natalie.'

'So you admit that it's all a mask you hide behind, then?'

He spared her a glance before he turned his gaze back to the treacherous track. 'We all hide behind masks of one sort or another. It's only the very young who face the world head-on, but even they soon learn to hide their feelings.'

His words made her ache, her emotions too raw to miss the poignancy of the brief, flat statement. 'But not everyone has as much reason to hide as you do, perhaps?'

'Meaning?' He arched a brow.

'That obviously you're involved in something you shouldn't be. What is it, Flynn? I want to know!'

He shook his head, his lips thinning. 'I have already told you that it's better you don't know all the details. I'm sorry you've been dragged into this, even sorrier for what happened, but as for explaining it all...' He shrugged. 'Maybe I'll be able to do so later, maybe not. We shall have to see.'

'And I shall have to be content with that?' She tossed her head, swinging the heavy tangle of hair back from her face. The sun had disappeared completely now, the sky along the horizon blood-red as night fell. 'I'm sorry, Flynn, but I need more than that. When we get back to Cairo I'm going straight to the police. Maybe they can persuade you to tell them the whole tale!'

'We aren't going back to Cairo.' His voice was edged with steel and he increased the speed until the Jeep was in danger of overturning as it rocked over the uneven ground.

Natalie had to grip hold of the door-handle to stop herself from being thrown out and was suddenly glad of its solid feel in a world which seemed to be hurtling out of her control. 'What do you mean we aren't going back to Cairo? Where...where are we going?'

'Into the desert.' He flicked his lights on to main beam so that they cut a swath through the darkness. In the glow from the dashboard his face looked harshly unfamiliar, the chiselled perfection of his features more pronounced than ever. It wasn't just the obvious differences of hair and eyes; it was as though suddenly the real man had been revealed.

Natalie fought to control a rising sense of panic but it was impossible. Too much had happened in too short

a time so that she could feel hysteria bubbling to the
surface.

'I want to go back to the hotel ... to the others. Damn
you, O'Rourke! Just take me back there!' She pounded
on his arm with her free hand and heard him swear
roughly as the Jeep skidded alarmingly before he
managed to bring it back under control. He slewed to a
halt, turning in his seat to pin her arms by her sides so
that she couldn't strike him again.

'Stop that, Natalie! You're getting hysterical.'

'Am I indeed?' She laughed out loud, the sound
shocking her because it sounded out of control. 'Am I?'
she repeated more quietly, searching his face with fear-
darkened eyes. 'I wonder why. Could it be because I'm
scared out of my wits by what's happened?'

He sighed harshly, his grip loosening although he
didn't let her go. Almost without conscious thought his
fingers slid up and down her arm in a soft, strangely
tender caress. 'I'm sorry, sweetheart. I know it's been
tough and you've been scared. I have too—scared I
wouldn't be able to find you, scared that when I
did——' He broke off, turning away without completing
the sentence yet Natalie knew what he'd meant. She gave
a small, eloquent shiver and heard him groan harshly
before he swung back and dragged her into his arms,
holding her so tightly that she could barely breathe,
although breathing was less essential than just being held
right then.

'When I realised what had happened, that you'd been
taken, I nearly lost my head! I knew there was something going on. I just didn't expect them to move so
quickly. If I'd had any idea that you would be in danger
then...' He drew her even closer, his cheek pressed
against the top of her head. Natalie had the feeling that

his holding her was not only comforting her but easing his own recent fears as well. She'd been afraid but so had Flynn, and a small glow of warmth started deep inside her at that thought, that he must truly *care* about her to feel that way.

'How soon did you find out I was missing?' she asked softly, shuddering as her lips accidentally brushed against his neck and sent sensations through every nerve in her body.

'Almost immediately, I imagine. Once I discovered you weren't at the nightclub with the others I went to find you. When you weren't in the suite or in any of the public rooms, I knew something was wrong even before I received that message informing me about the deal.'

His voice was hard and filled with a deep anguish at the memory of the moment when his worse fears had been confirmed. Natalie's hands slid up to his chest and rested there, wanting in some way to offer him comfort. She'd been scared and shaken and still felt that way, but had it been any easier for Flynn?

'Then what did you do? Did you call the police?'

He shook his head, easing her away from him as he sat back in the seat and stared through the windscreen. 'No. I knew that would put you in worse danger.'

'But why? What is this all about, Flynn?'

'What it is about is deceit and treachery which have had repercussions no one could ever have foreseen.' He laughed harshly. 'Even I didn't fully understand the dangers!'

Natalie shook her head in bewilderment, finding it impossible to make sense of what he said when she was still so much in the dark. 'If you didn't call the police then what did you do?'

'Luckily I have contacts. I used them, called in a few favours, and by sheer good luck discovered where you'd been taken. Now what I need to do is make certain that you remain safe until I can get you out of here.'

'You don't think they would...would try it again?'

His expression hardened at the note of alarm in her voice she couldn't disguise. 'These people aren't playing games, Natalie. The stakes are high and they'll stop at nothing to get what they want. They obviously saw you as the lever they needed to get what they want and that hasn't changed!'

'But it's so crazy. Why did they imagine that you would be willing to trade this thing...whatever it is...for me?'

'Because this act we've been putting on for Damian's benefit has been rather too convincing!' Flynn laughed sardonically at her gasp of shock. 'Yes, I see you're starting to get the picture. And when you look at it from their angle it does make sense. We've been sharing that suite at the hotel, acting to all intents and purposes as a loving couple, so they drew all the obvious conclusions.'

'Sense? It's madness.' She stopped, struck by a sudden unpalatable thought. 'That means that they've been watching us, doesn't it?'

'I imagine so.'

'Of course!' She gasped, her eyes huge. 'The man back there, the one who kidnapped me...he was the one in the hotel garden the other night!'

'I'm sure you're right. He might even have been the person who was in our suite, or there could be others involved. My contacts haven't been able to come up with a lot of information but it doesn't surprise me. These people are professionals, Natalie. That's why we cannot risk going back to Cairo, because that's the first place they'll look for you.' He swept a hand towards the darkness which surrounded them. 'Out here I can keep you a damned sight safer than I could there.'

'But what about the advert...David and the others?' Her head was reeling with all he'd told her, and all he hadn't, which was almost worse. What was he mixed up in? She wished she knew yet at the same time dreaded finding out!

'I told them that you'd had a message to return to England, a relative who's been taken sick suddenly.' He shrugged, his hands resting lightly on the steering-wheel. 'I used that as an excuse for your absence last night, told them that naturally you were upset and that I would be flying back with you today so no one would think it odd when I disappeared too. David was quite happy when I promised to get back late tomorrow to complete the job.'

'But won't that be dangerous? What's to stop those men from turning their sights on you now that this plan has gone wrong?'

It was impossible to hide the fear she felt at the thought of the danger he might be putting himself in. No matter what Flynn was mixed up in, she couldn't bear to think of anything happening to him!

'I can take care of myself. They'll have little chance of getting what they're after when they don't have you to use as a lever.'

'Would you have given it to them, then...this thing they want so badly?' Her voice was low yet she knew he'd heard her because he stiffened slightly, his hands tensing on the wheel before he seemed to make an effort to relax.

'Fortunately it didn't come to that, Natalie. So there's no real point in speculating on what might have been.

And once you're safely out of harm's way then we won't need to worry about it.'

The sense of disappointment she felt was strong, yet what had she wanted him to say—that he *would* have gone through with the exchange to have her returned safely? It might be ridiculous but she couldn't help wishing that were so! To know that Flynn cared that much for her safety would have gone a long way to easing the memory of this terrifying ordeal.

'I see.' She fought to keep her voice level, afraid that he would understand how she felt, for that was the last thing she wanted—to give him that kind of power over her. 'It seems you have it all worked out. So what happens next?'

'We shall spend the night out here then in the morning, once it's light, we'll drive to Farafra. I've made arrangements for us to be picked up there and taken on to El Khârga where a plane will be waiting. You will be flown out of the country to somewhere safe until I've got this sorted out.'

'But how long will that take? I can't just disappear! I have a job to do! What's going to happen about the advertisement? And what's Damian going to say when he discovers I've just upped and left?'

He swore softly, his face hard and set in the faint light. 'You're making a fuss over nothing.'

'It might be nothing to you, Flynn O'Rourke, but we're talking about my job here and it means a lot to me!'

'More than your life?' He caught her chin, forcing her face up to meet his angry eyes. 'This isn't a game of cops and robbers, Natalie. These men mean business. They don't care who gets hurt. Understand?'

'Oh, I understand all right. It's just that I'm not too certain which side you're on, Flynn. Are you one of the cops or one of the robbers, a goodie or a baddie?'

He let her go to start the engine. 'I'm sure you have your own theories on that, so I shall leave you to decide.' He cast her a hard look as he set the vehicle in motion. 'It will all be over and done with within a week, Natalie...one way or the other!'

A shiver ran down her spine at the tone of his voice, the harsh, unrelenting gleam in his eyes. She turned away to stare out of the window although there was nothing to see through the inky darkness. Would it really be over then? Perhaps this business might be sorted out, but just how easy was it going to be to put Flynn out of her life?

She glanced at him, watching the easy way he controlled the Jeep as it jolted along the track. She had no idea what he was involved in yet it seemed to matter less than the sudden realisation that very soon they would part forever. She should by rights be looking forward to that moment, now more than ever after what had happened, and the danger she'd been in because of him. Yet if she was honest then Natalie had to admit that she was dreading it. When the day arrived for Flynn to walk out of her life then he was going to leave a huge gap behind.

CHAPTER SEVEN

'WAKE up, Natalie! Come on...wake up!'

Hard hands shook her and she whimpered brokenly, her body racked with the icy spasms of fear. The man was coming closer now, gaining on her with every stride as she struggled through the sand. She chanced a glance over her shoulder and screamed shrilly, the sound turning to a keening wail of terror as she saw him just inches away, reaching for her...

'Damn it, Natalie, wake up! It's just a dream, honey.'

The deep tones finally cut through the fear and panic and her eyes drifted open, focusing hazily on Flynn's face. Shock ran through her whole body when she saw the haunted expression in his eyes. She reached out and touched his cheek, needing proof that what he'd said was true, that this was reality, not that terrifying nightmare scene which still lingered in her head.

Under her fingers his skin felt warm, faintly rough where his beard was starting to grow. Natalie let her hand linger for a moment then slowly let it drop to her side, staring up at him with eyes still shadowed by the images which had caused her to scream out in terror just seconds before.

Flynn swore softly as he drew her head against his shoulder and cradled it there with a hand which trembled. 'God, Natalie, I'm sorry! I should never have involved you in this in the first place!'

There was an aching regret in his voice which startled her. She drew back to search his face, wondering what he meant. The ordeal had been frightening but it hadn't in all honesty been Flynn's fault. He couldn't have known what those people had planned.

'You shouldn't blame yourself,' she said quietly.

'Shouldn't I?' He straightened abruptly, pushing the Jeep door open to walk a few feet away from where they were parked, his back towards her as he stared across the dark expanse of desert. It was nearly dawn and the moon was losing some of its brilliance, its silvery light subdued by the rising sun. It made it impossible to see his expression clearly but Natalie didn't need to see to understand the torment he was going through. He blamed himself for what had happened and was torturing himself because of it, and she couldn't bear to watch him suffering this way.

She got out and went to join him, not touching him as she stood by his side. She could feel the tension emanating from him and her heart ached for what he was going through. 'You didn't know that I was going to be kidnapped, Flynn. You couldn't look into a crystal ball and see into the future. Blaming yourself is pointless.'

'Is it?' He swung round, his face all stark angles in the faint light, the dye-darkened hair making him look even more like a stranger. He'd removed the lenses earlier and now his pale eyes glittered like moon-touched sea water. 'Perhaps I couldn't see into the future but I've learned enough about those people to know that they'll stop at nothing. I put your life in danger and that's something I can never forgive myself for!'

His pain hurt her; it made her ache to find a way to comfort him. Perhaps she should feel angry at him but she couldn't. Flynn was hurting and that was almost more than she could bear!

She laid her hand gently on his arm, feeling the muscles contract beneath her fingers in an immediate response which shook her so that the soft words of comfort died on her lips. She stared up into his face as an emotion as vast and expansive as the desert flowed between them, an emotion which touched her heart, her soul and every secret part of her, an emotion which both excited and scared her with its force and power.

Something of what she felt must have shown on her face because Flynn's fingers closed over hers to press them against his flesh as he stared back into her eyes. 'What is it, Natalie?'

'I... Nothing.' She dragged her hand away, turning her back on him, feeling shaken to the core by what had happened. She couldn't explain what she'd felt just now, didn't want to try because somewhere deep in her heart she was afraid of the answer. Yet just for a second her soul and Flynn's had met and joined and nothing would ever be the same again!

'For heaven's sake, Natalie, I know there's something——' He broke off so abruptly that she turned to look at him but he wasn't looking at her. He was staring past her, his eyes narrowed in such a way that alarm went skittering through her.

'What is it? What can you see?'

'Sandstorm.' He bit the word out, his face grim as she turned to look and gasped at what she saw—the huge, swirling black cloud of dust. 'It's heading this way and fast. We're going to have to get a move on, Natalie. We need to find shelter before it hits us.'

'Shelter? But can't we just get back in the Jeep?'

'No. That's the last thing we should do.' He strode past her and pulled a canvas hold-all from the back of the vehicle, quickly packing an assortment of items into it then tossing it to her. 'You take that, and bring that blanket. Wrap it around yourself, over your head as well.'

He bit the instructions out as he crammed more things into another bag, cutting off any further suggestions she might have made. Natalie did as she was told, spurred on by the urgency she'd heard in his voice, enveloping herself in the scratchy folds of the blanket as Flynn came back. He drew a fold of cloth over her shoulder and pressed it into her hand. 'When that dust hits, cover your nose and mouth. Understand?'

He pulled the hood of his robe over his head, then nodded towards a bare outcrop of rock several hundred yards away. 'We'll head for that. It should provide some protection at least but it's going to be rough. Whatever you do, Natalie, keep close to me, otherwise, you'll get lost so fast when that dust hits that I won't be able to find you again.'

He started towards the rocks, his long legs eating up the distance although he paused several times for her to catch up. Natalie struggled after him, the weight of the blanket hampering her progress through the sand. The wind was rising rapidly, screaming as it swirled around them. She glanced back, her heart pounding as she saw the dust-cloud just yards behind them, thick and grey, blotting everything from sight.

'Flynn...!' The first fine spray of sand choked off her cry of alarm, making her cough. Flynn must have heard, however, because suddenly he was beside her, his hand clamping around hers as he dragged her along with him.

'Cover your face as I told you to!' he ordered before pulling the hood of his robe across the lower part of his face.

Natalie did as she was told, dragging the rough cloth over her nose and mouth just as the full might of the storm hit them. The force of the wind was indescribable. It sent her staggering to her knees and defeated her attempts to get up until Flynn added his strength to hers. She felt as though she was smothering in sand, her eyes burning with its grittiness, each breath rasping painfully.

When Flynn bent and swung her up into his arms, she wanted to protest that it was too much for him to carry her, but she was too exhausted. She buried her face in his shoulder, her arms wrapped around his neck as he stumbled towards the rocks. Several times he fell but each time he struggled to his feet with a grim determination as he moved towards their goal.

Setting Natalie down, he dragged air into his lungs then dropped to his knees, pulling her with him against the rocks. They provided pitiful shelter but after the pounding of the wind it felt wonderful.

Struggling a knife out of his pocket, Flynn pressed his mouth against Natalie's ear. 'Move the blanket aside while I cut a strip off your dress.'

Natalie did as she was told without question, parting the folds of blanket while he deftly hacked a length off the red linen. Turning towards the shelter of the rocks, he pulled a bottle of water out of the hold-all and soaked the cloth then pressed it into her hand. 'Tie it over your nose and mouth as tightly as you can. It will help keep the sand out.'

Natalie did so at once, aware that Flynn was doing the same with another length of cloth cut from his robe, but it was so dark that it was impossible to see him now and panic rose swiftly.

'Flynn!' She reached frantically for him.

'It's all right. I'm here.' His hand was hard and wonderfully reassuring as it caught hers to draw her close. Reaching up, he drew the folds of the blanket over her head then turned her face into his shoulder, shielding her with his body as best he could as the storm raged around them.

It must have taken a couple of hours before the wind died down. When Natalie felt Flynn moving she lifted her head from his shoulder and pushed the blanket aside, struggling to free herself from the weight of sand which had built up all around them. The sky was growing lighter now, the silence after the noise almost painful.

Untying the sand-encrusted cloth from her face, Natalie tossed it away, grimacing at the gritty coating on her skin, which felt chapped and sore from the abrasive buffing.

'Here, rinse your mouth out a couple of times.' Flynn handed her a bottle of water, waiting until Natalie had finished before doing the same. He stowed the bottle back into the bag then stood up and shook the sand from him as he stared round then cursed softly.

Natalie stumbled to her feet, and followed his gaze then gasped out loud. 'Is that the Jeep?'

Flynn nodded, his eyes resting on what little could be seen of the vehicle above the dune of sand which had formed over it. 'It is. That's why we couldn't use it to shelter in. We would have been buried alive.'

Natalie shivered despite the increasing warmth of the sun, only then realising how lucky she'd been. Left to her own devices she would have instinctively sheltered in the Jeep and suffered the consequences of her ignorance.

Her face was unnaturally pale beneath the grit as she turned to Flynn. 'I can't believe it! How did you know it would happen?'

He shrugged as he bent to pick up the large hold-all. 'It's my job to know. Come on, we'd better see what we can salvage which might be of use to us.'

He started towards the Jeep but Natalie made no immediate move to follow him. She stared after him, frowning as she watched him striding through the sand. What did he mean, it was his job to know? Just how many more strings did Flynn have to his bow, how many more secrets was she yet to uncover? As she recalled what had happened before the storm, that strange disturbing surge of emotion they'd shared, it seemed more important than ever that she find out!

'We'll have to stop. I can't go another step!' Natalie slumped to the ground, wiping a hand across her wet forehead. Pushing the tangled mass of black hair from her eyes, she stared up at Flynn and could have wept at the unfairness of it all. He looked just as comfortable as if they'd been out for a pleasant afternoon stroll rather than this trek through the inhospitable desert landscape!

'We'll take a five-minute break, no more.' He dropped down beside her, squinting as he glanced up at the sun.

'Five minutes! Listen, O'Rourke, I won't be in any fit state to carry on in fifty-five minutes, so let's get that straight for a start!'

He leant back on his hands, his mouth curling tauntingly as he swept a glance over Natalie's flushed face. 'Not giving in that easily, are you, sweet?'

She glared back, used to his tactics by now. 'It won't work. This time you are not goading me into action. My legs feel like lead. If you want to carry on then feel free. But *I* am not going another step!'

She stretched full length on the ground, groaning as every over-worked muscle protested. They'd been walking for hours, their progress hampered every step of the way by the dragging pull of the sand. Natalie had no idea how far they'd come or how far they had to go, and didn't really care. She had gone just about as far as she intended to!

Strong hands caught her by the shoulders to haul her upright and hold her there. 'You, my sweet, are going to do exactly as you are told. Now get that pretty little backside off the ground and move it!'

Her eyes snapped open to glare into his. 'Make me! You're nothing but a bully, O'Rourke. I have gone as far as I can go and that's it. Understand?'

'You've gone as far as you *think* you can go, Natalie, but the human body is far more resourceful than most people give it credit for.' His eyes dropped to the mutinous curve of her mouth, darkening as they lingered on her cracked lips. 'So you want to stay here, do you? Then shall I tell you exactly what you can expect to happen to you?'

'I'm not interested! I'm not asking you to stay with me. You carry on. I'll wait here until someone comes along.'

He laughed with black humour. 'And just who are you expecting? The cavalry to come to your rescue? Sorry, sweetheart, but I doubt if there will be anyone along this route for... oh, the next month at a guess.'

Natalie stared at him in horror then shook her head. 'You're just saying that to make me do what you want. Someone is bound to come!'

'Why?' He swept a hand towards the vast, empty expanse of sand. 'Why would anyone want to come here? Tell me that.'

'I...well, we did!'

'Yes, we did. But think of the incentive we had for doing so, Natalie. This isn't some well-worn tourist route. We won't climb the next dune and find a busload of tourists snapping their pictures to take home and bore their relatives with. We're out here all by ourselves and it's up to us to get back.'

She didn't like his sarcasm one bit, the fact that he was obviously telling the truth even less! 'And exactly whose fault is it that we are in this mess? I didn't *ask* to be kidnapped! Nor did I ask to be brought out here into this...this wilderness while you performed your rescue! This is all your fault...every bit of it. If you hadn't got yourself mixed up in some sort of shady deal then we wouldn't be here in this mess!'

His eyes narrowed, twin shards of ice as they met hers. 'Is that a fact? So you aren't prepared to accept any of the blame?'

Perhaps she should have opted for a more diplomatic approach in the circumstances, but diplomacy had melted under the heat of the sun and the fire of her anger. 'Yes, it is a fact, and no, I am not to blame at all!'

His hands tightened on her shoulders, his mouth a thin, hard line. 'If you'd had the guts to tell Damian Renshaw how you really felt then none of this would be happening now.'

Natalie gasped at the sheer injustice of his accusation. 'How can you say that? You know very well that I couldn't offend Damian. I would have lost this account if I had!'

'If it means so damned much to you then I'm surprised you didn't simply do what he expected of you.' He smiled thinly as he watched her. 'You could have hopped into his bed and guaranteed that the contract was yours. Surely that would have been little enough price to pay for something you obviously value so highly?'

'Why, you...!' Natalie's hand arced through the air but before it could land a stinging slap on Flynn's lean cheek he caught her wrist, his fingers bruising. He bent towards her, his eyes burning with an emotion which made her heart shudder to a shocked halt, made her breath catch deeply in her chest.

'I think I warned you before not to do that, Natalie. You might not enjoy the consequences, although I would!' His gaze dropped to her mouth and stayed there in a look she could feel in every cell before abruptly he tossed her hand away and stood up. He barely glanced at her as he picked up the hold-all and slung it over his shoulder. 'Let's go. We've wasted enough time.'

He set off again, not bothering to look back to see if she was following. Natalie struggled to her feet, her legs shaking, yet the weakness owed less to exhaustion than it did to what had just happened. She hated Flynn for what he had just suggested, although even that paled in the face of what had happened next, the sudden, shocking realisation that he wanted her! She had seen it in the angry glitter in his eyes, felt it in her soul, and it shocked her because suddenly it forced her to evaluate her own feelings for him.

She wanted him too. She wanted to lie in his arms and feel his mouth on hers, wanted to savour the touch of his hands, the power of his possession. She wanted him as she had wanted no man before, not even Marcus, and that shook her world and left it spinning out of control!

They stopped as afternoon faded into evening. Natalie sank down on to the blanket that Flynn tossed on the ground, aching with exhaustion. When he offered her

the bottle of water, she shook her head mutely, too tired
even to make the effort to drink.

He swore softly then knelt beside her, unscrewing the
plastic cap and tilting the bottle to her lips, making her
swallow several mouthfuls. Putting it carefully down, he
pulled a foil packet from the bag and popped a tablet
out of it, dropping it into the palm of Natalie's hand.
'Take that.'

Natalie glanced at it then shot him a weary look.
'Trying to poison me now, O'Rourke?'

He grinned suddenly, white teeth gleaming against
dusty tanned skin. 'Tempting thought, sweetheart, especially when you're being awkward, but not today. It's
merely salt and vitamins to replace those you've lost
through perspiring.'

Natalie looked away from his handsome face, not
proof against the power of that smile as she would have
liked to be. She slipped the tablet into her mouth then
took another sip of water to wash it down. All afternoon
she had tried to reason with her wayward emotions,
telling herself that she had imagined what she'd felt
before, but her reaction to that smile made a mockery
of all her attempts.

'You're unusually quiet. Is there anything wrong? Or
perhaps you're hungry?' Flynn dug the rest of the flat
loaf he had produced earlier out of the bag and broke
a piece off to hand it to her with a faint grimace. 'It's
hardly sumptuous fare but it will have to suffice, and
there's some cheese and fruit left as well.'

Natalie bit into the hard bread and chewed it slowly,
accepting the fig Flynn offered her. 'You had it all
planned out, didn't you—food, water...everything?'

He rested back against the rocks, stretching his legs
in front of him as he tore off a piece of bread and studied

it for a moment. 'Nobody but a fool goes into the desert without making provision beforehand. It was something which was impressed upon us during training and I suppose old habits die hard.'

Natalie studied him curiously. 'Impressed upon you by whom?' She gestured towards the vast emptiness of the landscape. 'Most people wouldn't have the first idea about surviving out here. I know I haven't. Yet you seem to take it all in your stride and to have covered all the possibilities.'

'Not quite all, Natalie.' His voice was suddenly vibrant with an emotion which Natalie felt too, running in hot waves through her body. She took a small, desperate breath of air, wanting to say something to dispel the sudden tension, the feeling that events were moving out of her control. But then Flynn continued and she didn't know whether she felt relieved or disappointed.

'No one can foretell a sandstorm. They come out of nowhere and wreak havoc wherever they touch.'

Natalie looked down at the piece of bread she was holding, calling herself a fool. Perhaps Flynn did want her but that was all it was—a fleeting sexual urge. She was looking for excuses because she felt guilty and confused by her own feelings. But trying to convince herself that it meant more to Flynn than that wasn't the answer.

'It could have ended up far worse if you hadn't been prepared,' she said quietly without looking at him.

'Yes, it could.' He sighed wearily, pushing the dye-darkened hair off his brow. 'I was in the SAS. We were trained to work in all kinds of conditions. Desert survival was my particular field, though.'

'The SAS?' Natalie's eyes widened.

He grinned wickedly. 'Can't you see me in that role?'

'I...' She'd been about to say that she couldn't but stopped. She'd learned a lot about Flynn in the past few days even if she didn't have all the answers to the puzzles. Now, as she studied him in silence, it was less of a shock than it might have been to discover that he had once been part of that élite group. Behind that charming, handsome mask was a man of steel! 'Yes, I can. In fact I would go so far as to say that it suits you!'

He laughed out loud, easing himself comfortably against the rocky back-rest. 'I'm not too sure if that was a compliment or an insult, Natalie!'

She returned his smile, glad that the tension had eased because it bothered her that she should feel so confused. 'Take it which way you will. That's up to you. I merely meant that I'd suspected you weren't the easygoing charmer you seemed to be on first acquaintance even before I ended up getting kidnapped because of your nefarious dealings!'

His face sobered at her joking mention of what had happened, his eyes darkening. 'And that's something I shall regret to my dying day.' He held his hand up when she made as though to protest. 'No, don't say anything, Natalie. It should never have happened. I should never have allowed you to be put in such a dangerous position.' He gave a bitter, harsh laugh which tore at her heart. 'Not that this is much better!'

'It doesn't matter, Flynn.' She paused then gave a small shrug. 'Oh, I won't deny that I was scared when I woke up in that room; I can't remember ever feeling as scared if you want the truth. But it's over now. I just have to keep telling myself that and try to put it out of my mind.'

'You're right, but that doesn't stop me from blaming myself. I never wanted you to get hurt in any way, Natalie.'

The tender concern in his voice made her feel like crying. She forced a shaky smile. 'Is this another side to you, Flynn? There you are telling me that you were once in the SAS and, let's face it, they are known for their toughness, but maybe you aren't granite through to the core.'

He laughed deeply, a sound which sent a shudder of sensation through Natalie's body. 'Now, I don't want to give too much away and you, Natalie, seem to be getting to know me rather too well!'

'Oh, I doubt that! I don't imagine that anyone ever really gets to know you, Flynn. You merely feed people titbits of yourself, let them think they're starting to get to the heart of what makes you tick, but...!' She shrugged eloquently, her arm brushing his to send a host of disturbing messages throughout her nervous system before she hurriedly broke the contact.

'There haven't been many people I've ever wanted to afford that right to.' He paused deliberately, his eyes a deep, glorious green in the dying rays of the sun as they met and held hers in a look which sent a shimmering, incandescent excitement coursing through her. 'In fact, Natalie, you're the first, and God knows I didn't expect it!'

She didn't know what to say. The revelation seemed to have been torn from him almost as though he hated himself for the admission. It made her head spin, her heart feel as though it was being squeezed to death.

The silence lengthened, deepened, humming with emotions so raw that Natalie ached from their powerful assault on her senses. She closed her eyes, trying to break the spell, yet when she opened them again nothing had changed and all her uncertainties showed in the glittering depths of her eyes. 'Flynn, I...'

'Shh.' He laid his fingers against her lips, his eyes fierce yet achingly tender as they held hers in a look which told her he understood. 'Don't say it, Natalie. God knows this isn't something I planned but every word you say would be a lie, an excuse. And what we're feeling doesn't need excusing. It's as natural as breathing, as essential as eating and drinking, and far sweeter than either...!'

He bent towards her, intent etched on his face as his mouth came within a breath of hers. But with one last desperate burst of sanity Natalie pushed him away.

'No! You mustn't, Flynn, *we* mustn't!'

He ran his hand down her cheek, his fingers performing a seductive dance against her flesh which made the blood surge through her veins. When he ran the tips of his fingers across her mouth to trace its outline, Natalie gasped, a betraying sound which made his eyes glitter with a fierce kind of triumph.

'Mustn't, Natalie? Do you really think this is something which can be controlled by rules? Do you imagine a passion like this can be easily subdued?' He shook his head, his face a soft blur in the fading light. 'There are no rules now, just feelings. No rights or wrongs, just emotions. Nothing but the fact that I want you and, so help me, you want me!'

His mouth was hard and hot as it took hers. It gave no concessions, just demanded that she admit the truth. Yet she fought against it, a silent, desperate struggle against senses heightened to an unbearable degree, fought and lost when Flynn drew her into his arms and deepened the kiss.

'Natalie!' Her name on his lips broke down the final barrier, the tenderness, the aching need in his voice driving everything else from her head except that he was right—she did want him. She wanted him to hold her,

kiss her, show her the passion she could feel building
between them; she had realised that before and now she
knew the reason why. She wanted it because she loved
him.

The thought slid into her mind so easily, so softly that
Natalie knew that it had been waiting only for the
moment when she would admit it. She loved Flynn. She
had fought against the growing realisation for days, refused to look for answers too deeply, terrified of their
implications. Yet now that she had opened her heart and
her mind it was all so simple, all so clear. She loved him
and suddenly it made sense of so much which had recently been incomprehensible.

She slid her arms around his neck and parted her lips,
feeling the erotic sweep of his tongue around the curve
of her mouth before it tangled with hers in a rhythm
which mimicked what her body yearned for. Desire
flowed into every pore, hot, sweet, demanding a release
so that when Flynn's hand moved to the buttons on her
dress and eased them open she didn't resist. This was
what she wanted most, this physical outpouring of the
love she felt for him. She wanted to show Flynn how she
felt with her body before she told him later in words
which she could only pray he would want to hear.

The night air was cool on her skin as the dress fell
open but Flynn's hands were warm, his touch achingly
gentle, almost reverent as he eased the fabric down her
arms then unclipped the fastening of her bra. The moon
had risen now and its silvery rays lit the desert like a
stage, the black sky the backdrop to this sweet, heady
act of passion.

'You're beautiful, Natalie. So very, very beautiful...'
Flynn's voice faded as he ran his hand down her from
throat to waist, his fingers brushing the soft swell of her

breasts in the lightest of caresses, yet Natalie couldn't hold back the tiny cry which broke from her lips at the sweetness of his touch. She closed her eyes on a wave of sensation so strong that she could scarcely believe it, yet when Flynn repeated the gentle, devastating caress, his hand lingering to tease the peak of one breast into a rigid, throbbing point of desire, she knew it was very real.

Suddenly, in the middle of the desert, she was drowning. Waves of desire were closing over her head, sucking her down deeper and deeper... She clung to him, her hands tracing the corded muscles in his back and shoulders as she learned and savoured each curve.

He drew back, murmuring a swift reassurance when she moaned in protest, dragging off the robe and shirt and tossing them carelessly aside. He came back to pull her into his arms and mould her against the bareness of his torso so that their flesh merged, their heartbeats echoing each other.

Natalie ran her hands over his skin, letting it flow beneath her fingers like silk, warm, smooth and vital. Against her naked breasts she could feel the coarseness of hair, its abrasive touch making her nipples throb heavily.

When Flynn drew her down to lie beside him on the blanket before easing away the rest of her clothes, she watched his face, thrilling to the way his aqua eyes glittered possessively, his face contracting so that every line seemed to be etched like a sculpture. She reached up and smoothed her hands over the curve of his brow and cheekbones, the hard masculine perfection of his narrow lips, loving him at that moment more than she'd thought it possible to love anyone...

'Another mask, Flynn?' she queried tenderly, her voice a bare soft whisper in the desert silence.

He captured her hand to press a kiss to her palm before laying it gently on the blanket at her side as he turned her beneath him, his eyes holding a flame which made the excitement inside her flare. 'No masks, Natalie. Just you and me with nothing to hide behind now.'

She smiled as she brushed his mouth with an open-mouthed kiss, feeling the deep shudder which rippled through his powerful body, an echo of the one running through her. 'No, no masks now, Flynn, and no barriers,' she whispered.

And suddenly there was no need for words, no need for anything but the magic which rose and claimed them, carrying them far above the desert skies to undreamed-of heights.

CHAPTER EIGHT

MORNING came slowly, just a hint of red spilling along the dark horizon. The ancient Egyptians who had worshipped the sun and its god, Ra, had believed that each morning Ra sailed across the heavens in one of his barques, bringing the light with him. Natalie watched the slow tide seep across the sky and found it only too easy to accept that simple explanation. There was a timeless beauty about the desert landscape which defied modern attempts to explain its mysteries. If only she could remain here, away from the reality of life, but wishing wouldn't hold back the dawning day as Ra sailed on, or hold back what she had to face.

She closed her eyes and let her mind drift back to what had happened between her and Flynn the night before, feeling a strange mixture of joy and sadness. For years now she had believed that she was in love with Marcus, but last night had shown her how wrong she had been. Marcus had entered her life at a time when she had needed stability, someone to turn to, and he had always fulfilled that role. She loved him but wasn't in love with him and there was a world of difference between the two now that she'd had the chance to find out what love really felt like. Yet while she felt a heady joy to have discovered something so precious she couldn't help but feel sad at the realisation that Marcus's role in her life would be now irrevocably altered as he assumed the rightful position of a dear friend.

'Natalie.'

His voice barely disturbed the silence of the new dawn but Natalie felt her heart leap, her body tense. She looked round, flushing as she found Flynn watching her. He frowned as he crossed the space between them and dropped down to crouch beside her, his face darkening with anger as he studied her heightened colour, her sudden tension.

'Don't! There's nothing to be ashamed of. It wasn't wrong what we did, Natalie!'

He must have misinterpreted her feelings yet his words unwrapped a host of others she hadn't experienced up till then. She still had no real idea what Flynn felt for her but that hadn't prevented her from giving herself to him last night with an abandonment which still sent fire through her veins when she recalled it now. She looked away from his searching gaze, wondering hollowly what he thought of her, if he thought she *should* feel ashamed and that was why he had spoken of it.

'I...I never thought I could give myself to anyone that way,' she whispered brokenly.

The soft confession admitted so much and Flynn straightened abruptly, walking a little way away from her. 'Then I was right, Natalie,' he said harshly, 'You hadn't made love before?'

Her breath caught at the sudden note of fury in his voice. 'I... No. Are you angry with me for... for not telling you, Flynn?'

He stared towards the horizon, a tension about him she couldn't understand. Why was he so angry about her keeping her innocence a secret? It hadn't been deliberate; it had all happened so fast last night, that wild, abandoned passion flaring to life so that there had been no time for anything else.

'Flynn...?'

He swung round, his face shadowed as he stood with his back to the rising sun. 'I thought that you and Marcus were close.'

Her face flamed at the cold accusation and she glanced down as she pleated the ragged ends of her dress between nervous fingers, wondering why he was behaving like this, almost like a stranger. She loved him! Last night as they had finally drifted off to sleep in each other's arms she had made up her mind to tell him that this morning, buoyed up by a courage stemming from the passion they had unlocked in each other. Now she couldn't bring herself to make the admission to a man who was treating her like a stranger rather than the woman he had made love with just hours before!

'We are . . . but not in that way. Marcus thinks of me as a sister, nothing more.'

Flynn slammed one fist into the other, anger flowing from him, frightening her because she couldn't understand the reason for it. 'I don't understand any of this,' she said with a hard-won dignity. 'Neither your anger nor the fact that it seems to upset you that my . . . relationship with Marcus isn't what you imagined it to be. Just what is going on, Flynn? I think I deserve an explanation.' She gave a short, bitter laugh. 'Perhaps it's the only thing I do deserve!'

He took a step towards her, his eyes burning with a dangerous light. 'Meaning what exactly? That you feel guilty and wish last night had never happened? Well, my sweet, it's rather too late to have second thoughts now!'

It was the last thing she wished but she wouldn't tell him that, not when he was acting like this! His cruelty brought her to her feet, her face the colour of parchment now. 'Damn you, Flynn, how dare you presume to tell me how I feel? Maybe you're imbuing me with your feelings, seeking ways to excuse what you did?'

'Don't be ridiculous! This has nothing to do with what I feel but it has everything to do with you, Natalie!'

'Is that right? I beg to differ. I think you're the one feeling guilty this morning, and I wonder why? Could it be that last night was some sort of game to you? A way to find out if the old O'Rourke charisma was still as strong as ever!' She tossed her hair out of her eyes, cutting an oddly vulnerable figure in her ruined dress as she faced him proudly. 'Well, to set your mind at rest, I can tell you it's just as potent as it ever was! I fell for it, didn't I? So what better endorsement could there be than having a twenty-three-year-old virgin fall under your spell?'

She swung round with no idea of where she was going, only wanting to get away from him and from this pain which was tearing her apart. Yet before she managed more than a couple of steps Flynn was beside her, his hands hard and bruising as he swung her back and glared into her eyes.

'Oh, no, you don't! You're not getting away with that, Natalie. I never set out to charm you last night and you know it. What happened was a direct result of how we both felt, that desire which neither of us could control. You weren't seduced any more than you were raped. We made love because we *both* wanted to. And I'll be damned if I'll let you appease your guilty conscience now by laying the blame on me!'

'Why, you...!' She struggled wildly, her fists flailing at his chest as she sought to make him free her. He let her struggle, holding her until she was exhausted, his face unreadable in the sharp, clear light as the sun rose.

'You wanted me, Natalie, the same way that I wanted you.'

'No, I——'

He stopped the words with a kiss, his lips hard and unrelenting, intent on making her admit to herself what he already knew. Natalie turned her face away when he raised his head, tears sparkling on her lashes, and heard him utter a low oath under his breath as he turned it back and bent again, his lips gentle and achingly tender now as they parted hers.

Natalie wanted to tell him to stop, to make him see that this wasn't the answer, that they needed to talk and clear up all the silly misunderstandings, but the passion they had shared just hours before was building again, making her thoughts fragment.

Flynn drew back to stare into her face, his green eyes filled with an urgency he made no attempt to disguise. 'We made love last night because we wanted one another. That was the only reason and I want you to remember that!'

Why did she have the sudden feeling that it was important to him? And why did that fill her with a deep sense of foreboding she couldn't explain? 'Flynn, I...' She got no further, the words fading as did the thought when his mouth took hers in a drugging kiss which spun her back into the magic as though it had been minutes, not hours since they had last shared it.

When Flynn drew her down to lie beside him on the blanket and began to caress each soft curve as his lips drank from hers she moaned softly, a tiny, sensuous admission of his power over her, their power over each other. Each soft kiss, each slow caress built the fire, fanned the flames, sent the passion soaring between them, a passion which seemed more stunningly potent,

even more forceful than the night before because now
it seemed to be edged with a kind of desperation.

When at last they lay spent in each other's arms again,
the sun warming their skin, he stared deep into Natalie's
eyes. 'Remember this, Natalie. Never forget what we've
shared because this is what's real and important, nothing
else!'

She shivered, suddenly cold in the sun's golden rays.
She searched his face, wanting to understand what he
meant yet afraid to ask in case it damaged this precious
feeling they shared. Instead she opted for the truth as
she knew it now, the truth she wanted him to know: that
she loved him. 'I lo——'

He kissed her hard and hungrily, his mouth swal-
lowing up the soft confession, his green eyes dark when
they met and held hers. 'Don't say anything, Natalie.
Not yet, not now.'

Had he known what she had been about to say? Was
it something he didn't want to hear? The questions
haunted her as they dressed again and ate some of the
stale bread then set off. Natalie could feel them
drumming inside her head as the hours passed, an endless
rhythm which made her feel sick and hollow because of
their implications. She loved Flynn and had given herself
to him because of that, but had it been merely sex for
him, an appetite to be slaked like any other?

By the time they stopped at midday, Natalie's nerves
were raw with tension, her head throbbing. She sank
down on to the ground, resting her forehead against her
bent knees, avoiding looking at Flynn as he sat beside
her and pulled the bottle of water out of the bag. He
unscrewed the cap and took a swallow then handed it
to her, his face filled with so much concern when he saw

the pallor of her face, the lines of strain etched in it, that tears started to her eyes.

'What is it, Natalie?' Reaching out, he brushed the long strands of hair back from her cheek with a gentle hand. 'Are you feeling ill?'

What would he say if she told him yes, she did feel ill? Yet lovesickness wasn't a recognised illness; it didn't feature in any of the medical journals, she'd bet, but it was a painful ailment all the same!

'I'm fine,' she mumbled. 'Just tired.'

'It's more than that.' He turned her face to meet his searching scrutiny, swearing softly at what he saw. 'Natalie!'

The need to ask him was just too great. She closed her eyes and screwed up all her courage. 'Last night and... and before... was it... was it just sex for you, Flynn?'

The question seemed to hang in the air between them, stark and unadorned. Flynn's fingers tightened on her chin for a second then he groaned deeply, his voice rough with emotion when he finally spoke. 'No, damn it! It wasn't just sex, Natalie. You must know that!'

The joy she felt was so sweet that she could barely speak, but she didn't need to as her face said everything for her. When Flynn bent and kissed her, she returned the kiss with every scrap of love she felt for him, feeling the deep shudder which ran through his powerful body, the way his arms contracted convulsively around her so that she was locked against him. 'Natalie, I...' He stopped abruptly, and something about his sudden rigid tension alarmed her.

'What is it? Is something wrong?'

He moved her away from him, his voice emotionless when he answered. 'There's a car coming.'

'A car?' Natalie looked round, her first instinctive surge of relief fading as she turned back and saw Flynn's face. 'You don't think it could be those people . . . the ones who kidnapped me, do you?'

Flynn's hands balled into fists as he stood up and stared towards the cloud of dust churned up by the aproaching vehicle. 'It's possible. Whoever it is would need a damn good reason for being out here. In case it is I want you to do exactly what I tell you. Understand?'

Natalie nodded, her throat tight with nerves as she scrambled to her feet and stood beside him. 'Yes.'

'Good.' He picked up the blanket then nodded towards a small depression at the base of some rocks a few feet away from where they stood. 'Lie down there while I cover you with this. And don't move until I tell you to!'

'No! I'm not leaving you to face them on your own!'

His eyes went icily hard. 'I'll be a damned sight better off if I don't have to worry about you getting in the way! Now do it.'

Natalie did as she was told with ill grace, Flynn's tone stopping any other protests she wanted to make dead. He ignored her mutinous expression as he covered her with the blanket when she lay down. Natalie lay quite still, her heart pounding as she listened to the sound of the vehicle coming closer then the silence as the engine was cut, jumping when it was suddenly broken by a man's voice.

'You've led us quite a dance, I can tell you, O'Rourke. You're definitely going to pay for this!'

Natalie pushed the blanket aside, careless of all Flynn's orders as she reacted to the threat. Scrambling to her feet, she started towards the dusty Jeep and the dark-haired stranger standing next to it, her temper igniting to overcome her fear. He wouldn't find it so easy to deal with two of——

She stopped dead, her eyes widening as a woman suddenly appeared. She ran to Flynn and hurled herself into his arms, hugging him. He returned the embrace, swinging her off her feet while he kissed her soundly on the cheek.

Natalie's anger fizzled out like a damp squib, replaced by another emotion, not red this time but a definite shade of green! She had no idea what was going on, who these people were or anything about this scene she was witnessing. All she did know was that she would have preferred to see Flynn facing a whole posse of gun-toting villains rather than watch him hugging and kissing that woman!

The woman's name was Gabrielle. She was perhaps a little older than Natalie and extremely beautiful!

Lips compressed, Natalie sat in the back of the Jeep as they drove to El Khârga, trying to push the tormenting memory of Gabrielle in Flynn's arms to the back of her mind; only it refused to go. Just who was she? What did she mean to Flynn? They obviously knew one another extremely well if that whole-hearted embrace was anything to go by!

'Are you feeling OK?'

Natalie started nervously when a hand touched her arm, and gave the other woman a chilly smile. 'Fine, thank you.'

Gabrielle's face was full of concern but Natalie found it impossible to respond. It had nothing to do with how Flynn and Gabrielle had greeted each other, she told herself piously; it was the fact that she had no idea who Gabrielle and the man driving the Jeep were except that they must be mixed up in this sordid business. And that was hardly a recommendation!

Gabrielle gave a rather strained laugh, glancing towards the front as though seeking help, but the two men were deep in conversation. 'Well, I must say that you seem to be taking all this very well. Doyle was worried sick when you failed to turn up at the rendezvous. Once he heard about the sandstorm he wouldn't rest until we were on our way to find you.' Gabrielle shot a wryly affectionate look at the two men. 'One thing I can say, though, is if you have to get stranded anywhere then try to make sure that either my husband or Flynn is with you!'

'Your husband? You mean that you and Doyle are married?' Natalie couldn't disguise her surprise nor her sudden relief, and Gabrielle laughed gently.

'Mmm, very much so, and I happen to be crazy about him too!'

Natalie flushed, looking away from the friendly, teasing gaze. 'I'm sorry, but when I saw you hugging Flynn...' She tailed off.

'You put two and two together and came up with a round dozen.' Gabrielle patted her arm. 'I understand, Natalie. I would have felt exactly the same in your position. But despite how it looked Flynn is just a friend. And believe me, if Doyle thought he meant anything more than that to me then he wouldn't have trekked out here to dig him out of the sand!'

Natalie laughed despite her embarrassment. 'I'm sorry. I shouldn't have gone jumping to hasty conclusions, I guess.'

'I imagine it was a purely natural reaction.' Gabrielle treated Natalie to an old-fashioned look although her tone was bland. 'And you do have an excuse. You've been through quite an ordeal one way or another, haven't you, Natalie?'

Natalie sighed, her eyes turning to Flynn. 'I suppose so. The trouble is that I don't really know what's been going on. All I know is that Flynn has something the people who kidnapped me want desperately. Have you any idea what he's involved in?'

She held her breath but Gabrielle shook her head emphatically, leaving Natalie in no doubt that she was telling the truth. 'None. The first I knew about it was when Flynn telephoned Doyle the other night and asked him to fly out here immediately. But then Flynn always plays things close to his chest, as you probably know.'

Gabrielle leant forward to speak to her husband, leaving Natalie to ponder on what she'd said. The trouble was she *didn't* know Flynn in that way, and had no idea what he was mixed up in! It was crazy really; she had fallen in love with a man she knew absolutely nothing about!

By the time they drew up in front of the hotel where Gabrielle and Doyle were staying, Natalie was exhausted with thinking about it. She climbed wearily from the Jeep, stopping when Flynn laid his hand lightly on her arm to draw her aside while the others went in.

'Doyle is going to fly you out of here just as soon as he can. I've arranged for you to stay with him and Gabby for a couple of days until this is all sorted out. After that you'll be able to go back home and forget this ever happened.'

What did he mean by that? That she should forget about what they had shared as well because it was over now? Pain darkened her eyes as she gave him a tremulous smile. 'Will I? You imagine it's going to be that simple?'

His face tautened, his eyes silvery as they met her haunted gaze. 'I was talking about the danger you were in! The rest of what happened is something we need to discuss, Natalie, but not right now.' He smoothed a stray wisp of hair behind her ear with a gentle hand. 'Right now you need time to rest and recuperate from your ordeal. There will be plenty of time to talk, I promise you that.'

There was a tenderness in his eyes which made her heartbeat quicken, her blood race. Something of what she felt must have shown because suddenly his eyes darkened and he took a step towards her. 'Natalie, I want you to...'

'Natalie, do you...? Oh, sorry.' Gabrielle hesitated in the doorway with an apologetic smile. Natalie gave a shuddery little sigh, wishing that the other woman could have chosen a better moment. She'd had the feeling that Flynn had been about to tell her something then, something important, although she had no idea what it might have been.

Pinning a smile to her mouth, she turned to Gabrielle. 'Did you want me for something?'

Gabrielle smiled ruefully. 'I was just wondering if you'd like a bath before we set off.' She grinned at Flynn. 'And I imagine *you* won't be sorry to wash that dreadful dye out of your hair!'

He returned her smile, although it didn't quite dispel the tension Natalie sensed in him. 'I certainly won't. However, I've a few phone calls I need to make first.'

'Fine. Whenever you're ready. Doyle's somewhere about, I think. He'll show you which room we're in. Come along, Natalie. Let's get you out of those dusty clothes.' Gabrielle studied her assessingly. 'I should be able to find you something to wear as we're much the same size, I imagine.'

Natalie smiled. 'Thank you. That's very kind of you.'

'Not at all. Any friend of Flynn's is a friend of mine, as they say.'

Gabrielle headed back inside, leaving Natalie to follow her, but she hesitated, wondering if Flynn would tell her now what he'd been about to before. 'What were you...?'

'Go with Gabby, sweetheart.' He smiled at her, his green eyes glittering with an emotion which stole her breath and made her senses swim. 'We'll talk later.'

She turned and hurried inside, feeling shivers of anticipation rushing through her body. There had been something in Flynn's eyes just now which made her go weak just thinking about it! No matter what he was involved in they would work it out. They had to because she loved him!

Pulling the plug out of the bath, Natalie wrapped a towel around herself and sighed in pleasure. It felt marvellous to be clean at last! Picking up the bottle of moisturising lotion which Gabrielle had thoughtfully left for her, she started back to the bedroom then stopped when she heard the outer door open, and Doyle's voice. She opened her mouth to call out to him in case he didn't realise she was there then stopped when she recognised the answering deep tones. Her heart gave a foolish little lurch, sending the blood surging through her body so that for a moment she had to lean against the wall to regain her equilibrium.

'And you say that nothing has happened? Cole got the message we set up for him but there's been no sign of anyone checking the place out?'

Flynn's voice was hard-edged, carrying clearly to where Natalie was standing, yet wasn't the tone which froze her to the spot but the words. She drew in a soft little gasp of breath, her hands closing numbly on the damp folds of the towel. Deep inside a small voice was telling her to speak, to say something to alert the men to her presence, but she couldn't seem to form any words. What did Flynn mean? Why should he have sent a message to Marcus? And why did she have the sudden, awful feeling that it affected her in some way?

'No, there's been nobody around the place at all. Cole came back a couple of days ago and I did exactly what you wanted—made sure it got through to him where Alessi was supposedly being held, but...' Doyle sighed heavily '...I don't know, Flynn! I just have the feeling that you're barking up the wrong tree, that Cole isn't behind it as you thought.'

'Dammit, Doyle, he has to be! He's the only one who knew where Alessi was! The leak had to come from him, I tell you!'

'Maybe. I just wonder if there's something we've overlooked. Did you find out anything from Natalie about his contacts which could give us a lead?'

'No.' Flynn's tone was curt as he bit out the single word. 'I think it was a mistake bringing her into it. Things could have turned out a lot worse than they have.'

'Meaning her being kidnapped?'

'Yes!'

'Yet I think in a way that backs up this gut feeling I have about Cole. If he was working for them then would they have involved his girlfriend to such an extent?'

'She isn't his girlfriend, not in that sense, at least. In fact, I doubt our friends latched on to Natalie because of her involvement with Cole. I think the link was me.'

'I see.' There was speculation in Doyle's voice now. 'Then doesn't that cast a whole new light on things?'

'What do you mean?'

Natalie could hear the sharp edge of impatience in Flynn's voice, could imagine his expression, those aqua eyes glittering with frustration. She could see perfectly what his expression was, which was ironic because up till now her eyes had been clouded. Now it was as though a veil had been torn aside. Flynn had used her to try to find out something about Marcus! What could be clearer?

She must have made some slight sound, a small release of the numbing pain she felt—she had no idea—because suddenly heavy footsteps crossed the room and the door was thrust open. For a long moment Natalie stared into Flynn's face, unable to hide the agonising hurt she felt at his deception.

'Natalie, I didn't realise you were still in here,' he said tersely.

She gave a hard little laugh. 'I'm sure you didn't! Still, don't they always say that eavesdroppers never hear anything good?'

She pushed past him, barely glancing at Doyle who was standing by the bed. 'If you two will just give me five minutes then I shall get out of your way.'

Doyle shot a glance at Flynn, then turned and left the room without a word. Natalie stopped beside the bed where Gabrielle had left an assortment of clothes for her to try on. She tossed her long wet hair back, feeling the icy ripples of shock coursing through her system. It was only pride which stopped her from breaking down, only pride which kept her standing there staring defiantly back at Flynn, only pride that she had left now. 'If you don't mind...'

'How much did you hear?' he demanded shortly.

Natalie arched one black brow, pinning an artificial smile to her numb lips. 'Enough. Now please leave. I want to get dressed.'

He came across the room to her, anger thinning his mouth, glittering in the depths of his eyes. He must have managed to shower because his hair was once more restored to its usual blond, the light grey shirt and trousers he was wearing clean although they hung loosely on him. Natalie felt her traitorous senses stir even now, and turned away, unable to bear the agony of what she'd learnt.

'Just go, Flynn,' she said hollowly. 'There isn't anything left to say.'

He swore roughly, his hands hard on her bare arms as he swung her round so fast that she stumbled against him. He held her there, breasts pressed against his chest, thighs touching, seemingly unmoved by the sensations which were rocking her, reducing her pride to tatters. He had deliberately set out to trick her, used her to try to find out what he needed to know, yet she still wanted him!

'I'm not going anywhere until we sort this out!'

His arrogance was the spark needed to set fire to her anger and she fanned the flames, needing its burning heat to burn away all those other unwanted emotions. 'I think it's all been sorted out! I think for the first time since we met I actually have some idea what the truth is!'

She pushed him away, almost surprised when he let her go until it occurred to her that now he had no reason to hold her. She was of no more use to him, not now that she had discovered what he had wanted with her— a direct link to Marcus!

Pain cut through her heart, stealing every vestige of colour from her already pale face, making her sway for a moment before sheer courage steadied her. 'You tried to use me as a means to find out information about Marcus, didn't you? You saw me as the link you needed, someone with an insight into his life.' She laughed bitterly. 'No wonder you were angry when you found out just what sort of link we have, Marcus and I! Not what you expected, was it, Flynn? Did you hope that our pillow talk would include some indiscreet little snippets Marcus had told me which I would pass on to you?'

'It wasn't like that, Natalie! Making love to you had nothing to do with this!'

'Oh, spare me, please! Do you think I'm a complete idiot, Flynn?' She fixed him with a faintly rueful smile which cost a vast amount of effort to produce. 'It's a nice try but we both know it's just another of your smooth little lies. But I wonder what you're hoping to achieve by it? Keeping me sweet so that you can use me again at some later date to dig out more information?'

'I've already told you it wasn't like that! What can I say to convince you, Natalie?'

'Nothing. I wouldn't believe a single word you said, frankly, not when you're so adept at telling lies. So save your breath and spare me the embarrassment.'

'Then there doesn't seem to be a lot that I can do, does there?' He cut her an icy stare, his face revealing little emotion.

Natalie looked away, feeling tears stinging her lids, tears she refused to shed in front of him. 'No, nothing at all. I'd just be grateful if you would leave, Flynn.'

He swung round and strode to the door, pausing with his hand on the handle. 'You might not want to have anything to do with me, Natalie, but I want you to promise that you'll follow my instructions to the letter. Until I have this mess under control you could be in danger still.'

She didn't spare him a glance, staring down at her hands which were twisting the end of the towel. 'I wonder if it could be any worse than what has already happened?' She glanced up, holding her hand up when he made as if to come back to her. 'No! I'm not a fool, Flynn. I am aware of the position I'm in even though I can tell you here and now that whatever you suspect Marcus of being involved in you are wrong! You've just been wasting your time trying to pin the blame on him.'

He laughed harshly, face set and uncompromising. 'Such touching belief, Natalie! It's a great shame that Marcus doesn't know how highly you rate him!'

She looked at him, tossing her hair back so that it rippled in damp waves over her creamy smooth shoulders. 'Yes, isn't it? However, it's a mistake I intend to rectify just as soon as I can.' She laughed softly, hiding her grief behind a mask almost equal to those with which Flynn had deceived her. 'Some good might come out of this fiasco after all. You've opened my eyes to how easy it is to let life pass by without doing anything to get what you really want from it.'

'Meaning?' he asked steadily.

'Simply that when I see Marcus again I shall tell him how I feel.' She shrugged, her eyes holding his. 'I seem to have lost my inhibitions out in that desert, Flynn, so maybe I should thank you for that!'

There was a moment when his eyes seemed to burn into hers so fiercely that her breath stopped, held by the fury she could see in their depths. Then he swung round and walked out of the room.

Natalie sank down on to the bed, her body trembling, yet her eyes were dry now, the tears she wanted to shed gone. Nothing could ease this agony she felt, neither tears nor laments. It went bone-deep, maybe deeper. Deep enough to cut through to her soul, and nothing could go deeper than that.

'So you'll be in touch once you're sure it's safe?' Doyle picked up the lightweight grip and tossed it into the back of the Jeep.

'Yes. It should only take a few days but...' Flynn shrugged eloquently.

'But keep an eye open for anything unusual happening until we hear from you.' Doyle dusted his hands off then held one out to Flynn. 'Don't worry. We'll look after Natalie. Just look out for yourself.'

Flynn shook his hand and gave a tight grin. 'Concerned about me, Major? That must be a first!'

Doyle laughed as he slapped him on the back. 'Oh, I'm sure you'll survive. You always did have the luck of the devil. But you can't blame a man for worrying about his investments. You did promise me a cut out of this, I believe?'

'Doyle!' Gabrielle glared at her husband. 'That is the most awful thing to say!'

He slid an arm around her shoulders and kissed her lightly, his face so full of love that Natalie had to turn away as pain tore into her heart. 'Flynn and I understand one another, darling. He knows exactly what I mean.'

He glanced over Gabrielle's head, his face suddenly grave. 'Just keep your mind on what's going on and don't be side-tracked, though.'

Flynn's gaze followed his but rested only for a moment on Natalie before it moved away again, yet even that was enough to start her heart bumping painfully fast. She took a steadying breath, telling herself that it would be all over in a couple of minutes. Then she wouldn't need to see or speak to Flynn O'Rourke again! Yet despite what had happened and the way he had deceived her it seemed to be a hollow sort of comfort.

'Natalie.'

She started nervously, colour swimming into her face as she realised that he was addressing her. Desperately she looked round but the other couple were discreetly sorting the cases in the Jeep, obviously intent on affording her and Flynn a few minutes alone.

'Yes?' she asked brusquely. 'Although I don't think there's anything left for us to say to one another. To my mind it's all been said!'

His mouth thinned, his eyes glittering dangerously as he took a step towards her, standing between her and the Jeep. 'So you're still determined to close your mind to what I've been trying to tell you?'

Natalie didn't answer, turning away to stare along the dusty road, afraid that if she said a single word it would be just enough to break through the control she'd imposed upon her emotions. Flynn had used her in the cruellest way possible; how could she close her mind to that?

He sighed heavily, anger emanating from him. 'If I had the time then I'd damn well make sure——!' He broke off abruptly. 'I just wanted to tell you that I spoke to David before. He was panicking, as I thought he might be when I hadn't returned. Anyhow, I've smoothed things over with him and told him to expect me back there by this evening. I'm sure you'll be relieved to know that I do keep my word on some things, Natalie.'

She ignored the cutting edge of his sarcasm, staring quietly back at him, her voice devoid of all expression. 'Thank you.'

He made a small instinctive move towards her, anger flaring hotly in his eyes, before he obviously thought better of it. He smiled tightly. 'My pleasure, sweet. David gave me a message to pass on to you. It seems that Renshaw won't be joining the shoot after all. He fell and injured his ankle while getting off the plane in New York.' He gave a hard laugh which was full of a bitterness that made her ache. 'Seems that at least one of the reasons for my being here has been a waste of time, doesn't it? Let's hope I have more success on the other front.'

She couldn't bear to have him torment her this way! She started past him, her whole body tensing when he caught her by the shoulders and held her. 'Let me go!' she ordered in a hoarse undertone, conscious of the other couple just feet away. 'Damn you, Flynn, get your hands off me!'

His fingers tightened on her flesh, leaving marks. 'That wasn't what you said last night or this morning, sweet-heart. Then you couldn't get enough of my touch!'

The tears she'd struggled to hold back for so long suddenly welled from her eyes as she stared up at him. 'Damn you, Flynn!' she whispered brokenly. 'Damn you for what you've done!'

Pain flashed across his face. 'Natalie, you———'

'We'll have to leave now otherwise we'll miss our take-off slot.' Doyle drew their attention to the fact that they were ready to go.

Natalie pulled herself free of Flynn's hold, walking past him to the Jeep, uncaring what the others made of her tears. She climbed into the back, turning away as they pulled out from the hotel. She wouldn't look back. She didn't need to. She would never forget Flynn O'Rourke and how he had tricked her until her dying day!

CHAPTER NINE

THEY flew to Paris, Doyle piloting the small plane while Gabrielle tried to keep up a flow of conversation which gradually faded into silence when Natalie failed to respond.

By the time they arrived at the elegant apartment on the Avenue Victor Hugo, Natalie was exhausted, the emotional strain leaving her completely drained. The others ushered her inside then Doyle excused himself to make some phone calls, leaving the two women together.

'I'll show you straight to your room, shall I, Natalie?' Gabrielle offered in an over-bright tone. 'I'm sure you need a rest after all you've been through in the past few days!'

It was obvious that Gabrielle was alluding to the kidnapping and being stranded in the desert yet Natalie knew that it was neither of those which had left such a deep mark on her. She kept that to herself, however, following the other woman through the apartment to a large bedroom, a showplace of gilt and marble extravagance.

Gabrielle looked round with a grimace. 'We haven't redecorated in here yet. I'm afraid it's rather over the top, the taste of the previous owner. However, it seemed more important to do the rooms we use, especially the nursery, of course.'

Natalie summoned a smile, dropping her bag on to the bed. 'It's fine, thank you. I didn't know that you have a baby.'

Gabrielle's face filled with motherly love. 'Yes. He's with my mother at present, being dreadfully spoiled, I imagine.' She crossed the room to switch on the gilded desk lamp and laughed softly. 'He's the apple of her eye despite the fact that at just one year old he can be a handful!' She cast Natalie an amused look. 'We decided to come to Paris for a second honeymoon, actually. The first one ended up for three as John had just been born!'

Natalie's smile faded. 'And it seems to be turning into a repeat now that you've been burdened with looking after me.'

'Nonsense! Doyle and I are delighted to help out.' She gave Natalie a searching look. 'Tell me to mind my own business but you seem very unhappy, Natalie. Is it just because you're worried about Flynn? If it is then believe me when I say that he's more than capable of looking out for himself!'

She didn't doubt that. Flynn O'Rourke had priorities and they always came first, his main aim in life to achieve his goals no matter what he had to do! She dropped her gaze to her hands, hiding the sudden easy tears which filled her eyes, grasping gratefully at the excuse Gabrielle had offered her. 'You can't help worrying,' she said obliquely.

'I know. I worry about Doyle a lot of the time but one consolation is that both he and Flynn are highly skilled at what they do. There isn't much that they can't handle.' She gave a small shrug, taking a last look around the room. 'Still, what you need now is some rest. I'll see you later.'

She left the room, closing the door behind her. Natalie got up from the bed and walked over to the window, pushing aside the sheer lacy curtain to stare down at the street below. It was rush-hour and the cars were bumper to bumper, engines revving noisily. She'd been to Paris several times yet suddenly it felt as though she was seeing it with unfamiliar eyes. She felt different, changed in some way, but was it any wonder after what had happened? Flynn's advent into her life had changed it irrevocably. Now she had to wait until the message came from him before she could try to rebuild it, but it wasn't going to be easy.

It was the third morning of her stay. Natalie got up, taking her time showering and dressing. There was nothing to rush for—the long days spent in the apartment dragged.

There was a pot of coffee keeping warm on the stove when she entered the kitchen but no sign of Gabrielle or Doyle, which was unusual. The couple had been assiduous about keeping their promise to look after her, refusing to leave her by herself despite her protests that she would be all right. Natalie felt guilty that their holiday was being spoiled by her presence but all her reassurances fell on seemingly deaf ears. When would Flynn make contact and end this misery for all of them?

'Hello, Natalie.'

The shock of hearing his voice was so great that the cup of coffee she'd just poured slipped from her hand. It smashed on the white tiles, spraying coffee all over the floor, but Natalie was barely aware of it. She just stared at the figure in the doorway, feeling a whole maelstrom of emotions pouring through her, erasing the numbness which had filled her these past few days to leave her suddenly painfully vulnerable once again. It was only when she heard Flynn make some sharp exclamation of concern that she tried to collect herself.

'I had no idea you were here.'

'So I see. I'm sorry. I didn't mean to startle you. I arrived about an hour ago when you were still asleep.' He moved into the room, casting a quick look down at the floor. 'I'll clear that up; you sit down.'

She didn't need him telling her what to do and when to do it! She didn't need him interfering in her life ever again! 'Thank you but I'm perfectly capable of doing it myself. My mess, my place to clear it up!'

His eyes narrowed but he said nothing as he pulled out a chair and sat down at the table, watching her while she tore a length of paper towel off the roll and bent down to mop up the floor. 'How have you been, Natalie? Have you got over what happened to you; you aren't still having nightmares about it, I hope?'

He meant the kidnapping, of course, not what *had* been giving her sleepless nights of late. And how did anyone ever get over discovering that the person you loved had deceived you as Flynn had deceived her? Yet there was no way she would ever tell him that! She stood up abruptly, knocking against the table in her haste.

'Careful!' He shot to his feet, the feel of his hands at her waist steadying her so familiar that Natalie stilled as her body was flooded with sensations and memories of all those other times...

'Natalie, I...'

'Excuse me.' She pushed him away, her heart thundering, aching with a bitter pain which made her feel sick. She turned her back on him to rip another length of paper towel from the roll, waiting until her hands had stopped shaking before she returned to the task of clearing up the coffee.

Flynn sat down again, leaning back in the chair, but there was a tension about him which flowed between them, linking them as she didn't want to be linked to him ever again. He had tricked her, used her, yet even now she could feel the magnetic pull of his attraction and felt ashamed.

'I'm sorry, Natalie. You might not believe me but what happened between us in the desert wasn't part of my plan.'

Did he really imagine that she wanted to discuss it? She tossed the soiled towel into the bin and swung round, wanting only to get away from him and all the memories he was evoking. But it seemed he had no intention of sparing her this final humiliation as he stood up and moved in front of her to stop her leaving the room.

Her eyes blazed defiance. 'I am not interested! Can't you get that into your head? I've listened to all I intend to listen to. Now all I want to know is if it's safe for me to go back home and get on with my life!'

'You're the stubbornest, most infuriating woman I've ever met! Damn it, Natalie, why won't you try to understand?'

She laughed harshly, an ugly sound which rang around the kitchen and held the faintest thread of hysteria before she cut it off abruptly. 'I understand everything! Would you like me to explain it to you?'

He shook his head, his eyes pale and glittering with impatience. 'I don't need you to explain——'

She cut him off, gripping his arms when he made as though to move away from her. 'Oh, but I disagree. I think you *do* need me to explain it to you, nice and clearly so that you're left in no doubt that I understand what's been going on!'

'If it makes you feel better...' He shrugged almost indifferently, faint amusement in his voice now. He glanced pointedly down at where her hands were holding his forearms then calmly walked across the room to pour himself a cup of coffee when she let him go. 'Well, Natalie? Let's hear it, then.'

He had taken the impetus from her, making her feel as though she was acting like some sort of silly, hysterical woman! She swung away from him, forcing the bile from her throat, wondering what to say now, and heard him laugh tauntingly.

'Cat got your tongue now, sweet? Why so reticent all of a sudden? You were dying to tell me a minute ago so what's stopping you now?' His voice dropped a note, deep and disturbing as it flowed across the room. 'Could it be that you've suddenly seen sense and realised what I've been trying my damnedest to make you understand?'

'Yes!' She swung round, hair flying around her shoulders before she pushed it back with an impatient hand. Anger was runing along her veins like electricity, giving her the power now to stand there and face him, to let him know what she thought of him for his deceit and treachery. 'I have seen sense, Flynn. I saw it three days ago, a blinding flash of insight into what had been going on. My only regret is that it didn't happen sooner!'

'Why? Do you honestly believe that it would have made any difference? You think you've uncovered all the facts but if you had found out a day earlier do you *really* imagine it would have stopped us making love?'

His arrogance took her breath away for a second and then she found her voice. 'Of course it would have made a difference! If I had known that you were using me as a means to investigate Marcus then I would never have slept with you! I couldn't have stood for you to touch me if you'd like the truth!'

'Is that a fact?' He was across the room and reaching for her before she realised what he intended, his aqua eyes holding a light which made her fight him instinctively.

'Don't you dare, Flynn!' she spat out, quelling the sudden shaft of excitement which shot through her as his hands slowly closed over the delicate bones of her shoulders.

He laughed deeply, bending so that his face was just a blur as he came closer. '"Who Dares Wins"...that's the motto I lived by for quite a few years, Natalie. It's one which still holds true, I think!'

His lips were warm and hard and totally devastating. The kiss was a deliberate assault on her senses, a skilful playing with her emotions. Natalie tried to close her mind to the erotic feel of his mouth nibbling hers, the soft, seductive sweep of his tongue around the tightly pressed contours of her lips. It was the sweetest kind of torture imaginable, to stand in Flynn's arms and feel him kissing her this way, but somehow she had to resist him for the sake of her own self-respect. She could never live with herself if once again she fell victim to his manipulative powers!

'No!' She pushed him away with a strength which came from desperation. 'I won't let you do this, Flynn! I won't be manipulated by you ever again! We both know why you slept with me. I only hope you think it was worth it!'

His eyes were glittering green shards of ice as his anger rose and matched hers. 'Oh, it was worth it, Natalie, but maybe not in the way you mean!' He skimmed a look over her rigid figure then smiled in a way which made her go cold. 'You may have been a virgin, my sweet, but your response was everything any man could wish for.'

How she hated him for reminding her of that! It was bad enough facing up to *why* Flynn had slept with her without having it pressed home just how eagerly she had responded to his lovemaking! Shame drained the colour from her face and she looked away. She heard him curse harshly.

'Damn it, Natalie, why won't you listen to what I'm telling you?'

'Because I don't want to hear another word you have to say about the whole unsavoury episode!'

'Unsavoury? Is that how you view it?' There was a warning inflexion in his deep tones but she chose not to heed it.

'Yes! How else? I bitterly regret it ever happened.'

'And you're not prepared to trust me at all?'

'Trust!' She laughed hollowly, staring at him with disbelief. 'After the way you lied to me? What do you take me for? A complete fool?' She tossed her hair back and faced him proudly. 'Save your pretty speeches for someone who will believe them, because I don't. I know exactly what you're like now, Flynn!'

'You don't know me at all, Natalie, at least not in any way which counts.'

If anything Natalie went paler as the words hit home. She and Flynn knew one another in the most intimate way possible between a man and a woman yet it meant nothing to him. What a fool she had been, a stupid, blind fool, to be taken in that way!

'Perhaps I don't, Flynn. Perhaps I no longer want to know you! So let's not bother wasting any more of our time. Now, if you have finished . . .'

'I have.' He searched her face for a long moment then looked away as though suddenly tired of the conversation. 'I don't think there's anything left to say either.

Oh, apart from the fact that all the work on the advertisement has been completed. David seemed quite pleased, if it's any consolation.'

'And how about your other "job", Flynn?' There was ice in her voice now, put there deliberately to hide the pain which was slowly ripping her apart. 'Have you found out who was behind this trouble you've had? And if you still tell me that it was Marcus I have to say that I won't believe you!'

'Marcus is a lucky man to have someone who believes so implicitly in him.'

'Not lucky.' Her heart was heavy as she stared quietly back at him. 'Marcus has earned my trust.'

'As I never could, eh?' He gave a faint self-deprecating laugh, his mouth curled derisively. 'I get the picture, Natalie. But to answer your question, I am certain now that Marcus didn't pass on the information himself.'

'I see. I suppose it would be too much to expect you to tell me what has been going on and what this information actually was?'

He shrugged. 'There are still a lot of things which need sorting out before I get to the bottom of it so I prefer not to go into any detail right now. Suffice it to say that it's under control and that you're safe to go back home.'

She laughed with scant amusement. 'Ever the master of the evasive answer, eh, O'Rourke?'

'I've just tried the truth but that didn't meet with an enthusiastic reception, so can you blame me?' His eyes seemed to bore straight into her for a moment, searching for...what? Natalie had no idea but he seemed not to find it because he suddenly turned and walked across the room, pausing in the doorway to glance back. 'I suggest you try to forget what's happened. I know I shall do my best to do so! Take care, Natalie. I hope that things work out as you want them to between you and Marcus.'

He had gone before she could try to stop him, the front door closing quietly behind him. Natalie bit her lip, feeling the tears welling in her eyes. So that was it, the end of it all. She and Flynn wouldn't meet again. If there were any problems which needed sorting out concerning the advertisement then she would ask Guy to handle them. Flynn had used her, tricked her, but suddenly the thought that he would no longer be a part of her life seemed to be tearing her apart!

'Natalie? Has Flynn gone already? I thought that… What's wrong?'

Gabrielle's voice held a sharp note of concern which was reflected by the sympathy on her face. When Natalie murmured a choked excuse and ran to her room, Gabrielle followed her.

'Want to tell me about it?' she asked softly, closing the door.

Natalie wiped at the tears on her cheeks but it didn't end the flow. 'There's nothing to tell. Flynn came to tell me that it's safe for me to go home. Now he's left.'

'And was that all he had to say? I thought that he…' She shrugged then treated Natalie to a steady look. 'I had the feeling that you and Flynn had become…close in Egypt.'

Natalie flushed and looked down at her hands. 'Yes.'

'So what went wrong?'

'Nothing *went* wrong. It was wrong from the outset!' Her voice shook and she breathed deeply to steady it. 'Flynn used me as a means to find out information about Marcus Cole. He knew that Marcus and I are friends but unfortunately got the idea that we were more than that!' She laughed bitterly, pain echoing in the raw sound. 'It's a pity he didn't check his facts a bit better before he made the ultimate sacrifice!'

Gabrielle went and sat down on the end of the bed, watching Natalie with wide, shocked eyes. 'You don't honestly believe that Flynn slept with you to get information from you?'

Natalie looked away. 'What else should I think?'

Gabrielle shook her head. 'No. I don't know what's gone on but I can tell you here and now that Flynn would never do such a thing!'

'How can you be so certain?' Natalie walked to the window then came back again. 'He had it all planned out from the moment he heard a message I left on Marcus's answering machine. He inveigled himself into my life, got himself hired by my firm, all with the sole intention of gaining the information he wanted!'

She laughed again but there was an ache of sadness in it this time. 'The fact that he's realised now that he was mistaken about Marcus just adds the crowning touch, don't you think, to the whole miserable fiasco?'

Gabrielle got up slowly. 'I don't know what to think. I do know, though, that Flynn would *never* have used you that way! It might be a highly unfashionable word but he is an honourable man, just as Doyle is. Yes, both of them will push themselves to the limit to get what they want but to do such a thing...!' Gabrielle's face was filled with a deep assurance as she treated Natalie to a level look. 'But one thing you haven't explained is *your* reason. Why did you allow it to happen, Natalie? Are you in love with Flynn?'

'I... Yes, but that doesn't make a scrap of difference!'

'Oh, I disagree. I think it makes all the difference in the world, Natalie. You see, I've known Flynn a while now and in that time I've seen him with any number of women.' She must have seen the small grimace Natalie gave because her smile was gentle. 'Flynn is handsome and charming and wonderful company, and probably the hardest man in the world to get to know because he keeps his emotions so well-hidden. And today when he arrived was the first time that he's let the mask slip... when he was speaking about you!'

'But he used me... tricked me...!'

'And spoke about you to Doyle and me in a way he has never spoken about any woman! So if you love him as you say you do then think long and hard about what you're about to lose. Perhaps he did start out with an ulterior motive, but I have a feeling that things changed, perhaps more than *he* expected them to!'

Gabrielle gave her a last, knowing smile then quietly left the room. For a long time afterwards Natalie stood staring into space. Was it possible that Gabrielle was right and that Flynn did feel something for her? She savoured the idea greedily then slowly common sense reasserted itself. If Flynn felt anything at all for her then he would never have deceived her the way he had. She was a fool to hope for something which could never be. She loved him and her life would never be complete because he was no longer a part of it but it was better to face the truth than keep on wishing for the moon!

'It was the most awful nuisance having it happen just then, Natalie. I couldn't believe that fate could be so unkind to us.' Damian patted her arm, letting his hand linger until Natalie got up from the desk and effectively broke the contact.

She crossed the room and stopped beside the table, her hand resting lightly on the large folder lying on it. David had sent the photographs over about an hour before but she hadn't looked at them yet. She had been putting off the moment but now that Damian was here she couldn't delay it any longer.

'Natalie?' There was a faintly peevish note in Damian's voice now and she sighed as she hastened to respond.

'It must have been dreadful for you, Damian. Ankle injuries can be extremely painful.' She forced just the right note of sympathy into her voice as she opened the binder and started to arrange the prints along the table, trying hard not to look at them. She had been back for over a week now but although she had thrown herself into her job it hadn't helped ease this sense of loss she felt, the nagging pain which was always with her. She missed Flynn and nothing could alter that.

Damian seemed only slightly mollified as he came to join her. 'Yes, I was in the most tremendous pain. That's the reason why I didn't fly on to Egypt. Were you as disappointed as I...? Good lord! Isn't that that O'Rourke fellow?'

Natalie was glad of the sudden shift in conversation although she could have wished for something else to distract Damian from the track he'd taken persistently since he had arrived. She steeled herself then glanced down, feeling her heart lurch unsteadily. David had told her over the phone that the photos had turned out well but that hadn't prepared her for the impact they made. It was arguably the best work David had ever produced, and definitely the most stunning justification of her own talent. Yet as her eyes came to rest on the final print all that faded from her mind.

The picture obviously wasn't to be used in the campaign; David must have taken it on impulse, drawn by the powerful statement the subject made. It showed Flynn standing on a rocky outcrop staring across the desert. The wind was blowing his hair back from his face and plastering his clothes to his body so that every lean, strong line was emphasised. There was no hint of that urbane charm now, that cool sophistication he used to such effect. He looked what he was: strong, tough, self-reliant, a man few could equal; the man she was in love with, the man she wanted to spend the rest of her life with. And suddenly in that instant she knew that she couldn't let him go without finding out if Gabrielle might have been right! That Flynn might actually care for her was too precious a prospect to ignore because of pride.

'I must say this seems all highly irregular! Why wasn't I informed that O'Rourke was being used in the promotion?' Damian's tone was openly belligerent and hastily Natalie tried to get her thoughts under control and deal with him before she could deal with something far more important!

'I'm sorry if you're annoyed, Damian. However, I think the photographs fulfil all our expectations and will make a tremendous impact.'

'I'm not saying they aren't good,' he admitted grudgingly. 'It's just the fact that I wasn't informed!'

She could feel her impatience building but curbed it, reminding herself that if it hadn't been for Damian she would never have met Flynn at all! 'Flynn agreed to help out when the original model fell ill. I cleared it with your marketing director in your absence.' She took a deep breath then plunged on, knowing that it had to be said. 'However, I have to confess that it suited me at the time to use Flynn, although not for the reasons you imagine.' She held Damian's gaze levelly. 'Flynn and I were not romantically involved when you met him at the opera that night.'

'Not involved . . .? But you made a point of telling me
that you were!' Damian was flushed with bad temper
now but Natalie stood her ground, wanting only to get
this over with so that she could concentrate on what she
should do next, something which made her heart beat
furiously at the thought.

'I was aware that you were exhibiting a certain interest
in me, Damian, so I decided to do something about it.'

'Something . . . well, I . . .' Damian blustered and then
his face suddenly cleared. He ran his hand over his
thinning hair with a rather arch smile. 'I think I'm
starting to understand, Natalie. You decided to use
O'Rourke to make me jealous! Naughty girl, although
I must confess it isn't the first time a lady has gone to
such lengths!'

'Oh, but——!'

Damian held his hand up. 'Not another word, my dear.
I don't want you to feel at all embarrassed. It won't alter
our working arrangements one jot.' He glanced at his
watch then headed for the door, patting her arm in a
purely reflex action which held no trace of real interest
now as he passed her. 'I really must fly. I shall leave it
all in your capable hands, Natalie. Have a word with
Marketing if you need anything.'

He was gone before Natalie could blink, let alone try
to make him understand how wrong he was! She drew
a long, incredulous breath. It had all been so *simple*!
Damian's interest in her had waned the very instant he'd
reached the conclusion that she was interested in him.
It was the chase he enjoyed, not the capture! Oh, how
she wished that everything else could be worked out so
easily!

She went back to her desk and dialled the number to
Marcus's flat but the call was redirected to the porter

who informed her that Mr O'Rourke had moved out. Natalie thanked him, replaced the receiver, and put her head in her hands in despair. Where should she look for Flynn now? He had mentioned something about having a place of his own but she had no idea where. What should she do?

'Natalie? You OK?' At her nod of assurance, Guy rushed on, not bothering to come into the room, merely sticking his head a bit further around the door. 'I've just had that firm on the phone again so do you think you can handle it now that the Renshaw account is in the bag?'

'Which firm?' she queried hazily, her thoughts elsewhere.

'That couture house from Paris. Remember?' Guy was already starting to leave. 'I'll leave it with you.'

Natalie stared at the empty doorway, feeling as though she'd just been struck by a thunderbolt. Paris! Of course. She picked up the phone again as she hunted a slip of paper from her bag, a smile playing around her mouth. It had worked once before almost alarmingly well and with undreamed-of consequences. It was definitely worth seeing if it would work again!

CHAPTER TEN

THE morning was pleasantly warm. Natalie opened the French windows and carried her coffee out on to the balcony while she watched the heavy London traffic rushing past. Pushing a stray wisp of hair back into the loose knot she'd caught her black curls into, she leant against the railing and tried to control her nervousness. She must have gone over it all a hundred times since she'd made that phone call but it didn't help ease the sense of panic at the realisation that Flynn might be furious once he discovered what she had done!

The doorbell suddenly rang and the blood drained from her face. With shaking hands she set the cup down and hurried to answer it but it was only her elderly neighbour to ask if she would accept a delivery for her while she was out.

Assuring her that she would be happy to, Natalie went to close the door then stopped when a man suddenly appeared at the top of the stairs. For a blank moment she just stood and stared at him then took a choking little breath as he strode over and hustled her back inside the flat.

'Have you no sense? What were you doing standing out there where anyone could see you?'

His voice was hard with anger, his body tense as he glared at her from furious aqua eyes. There were deep lines grooved from his nose to his chin, the glint of golden stubble on his jaw, tiredness etched into every weary line,

162

but to Natalie he was the most marvellous sight she'd seen in ages!

'Hello, Flynn,' she said softly, 'How are you?'

He ignored the greeting, striding past her with a muttered imprecation as he spotted the open window. He slammed it shut then turned back to her. 'Now I want you to tell me exactly what's been going on. Where did you see that man? And how long had he been following you, do you think?'

Authority echoed in the terse questions and Natalie looked away, wondering how to explain that it had all been a ruse to get him here. She had phoned Gabrielle in Paris and played the part of her life as she'd told her that she was being followed. It had been a gamble but one that had paid off because Flynn was here as she'd wanted him to be. But how did she go about confessing what she'd done?

'I... would you like some coffee? I was just going to make a fresh pot.' With a cowardly need to put off the dreaded moment, she started towards the kitchen only to come to an abrupt halt when she found him standing in her way. He glared down at her in a way which was less than reassuring, his face set into grim lines of strain, and Natalie swallowed down a groan. He was going to be really mad when he found out how she had tricked him!

'I don't want coffee! I drank more damned cups of coffee than I can count on the flight over here from Brazil!'

'Brazil! You... you were there when Gabrielle passed on my message?' Natalie's eyes widened in horror as the enormity of what she'd done hit her hard.

'Yes. I'd only arrived an hour before the call came through. I booked myself on the next flight out so no,

Natalie, I don't want coffee or anything else apart from hearing what's been going on! Let's take it from the beginning, shall we?'

'There...there's nothing to take,' she said huskily before her courage failed her completely.

'You might think there isn't but allow me to be the judge of that.' He slammed his fist into his hand, anger darkening his eyes. 'I would have sworn that there would be no repercussions for you! But that just goes to show once again that you can't be over-confident in circumstances like these!'

'You weren't—over-confident, that is.' Natalie took a deep breath and closed her eyes as she forced the confession out. 'There's nothing to tell you, Flynn, because nothing has happened. There's been nobody following me. I...I made it all up!'

'What?' His fingers dug into her shoulders through her thin lilac cotton shirt and Natalie winced. However, he didn't relax his grip, just shook her none too gently until her eyes flew open to meet his angry, incredulous stare.

'I made it up. I telephoned Gabrielle and told her that tale about being followed but it wasn't true.'

'Why? Just what sort of a game are you playing, Natalie? You drag me back here with some cock-and-bull story then calmly stand there and tell me that you made it all up!' He bent towards her, his face taut with anger. 'So help me you'd better have a damned good reason for doing it!'

She had! The best reason in the world, but he would need to stop shouting and answer a few questions before she ever told him what it was.

Natalie glared back at him. 'Threats, O'Rourke? Perhaps the company you keep is starting to rub off?'

'I wouldn't get smart if I were you, honey. I would tread extremely carefully for the next few minutes, if you want my advice.'

'And why would I want that? You don't seem to me the best person to be offering advice, not after all the trouble you got me into!'

'Why, you little...!' His hands were bruising as he hauled her to him so fast that she slammed against his chest. 'I ought to put you across my knee for that! It's way past time that someone taught you a lesson!'

Natalie's breath whispered from her, her eyes lifting to his. 'Like the lessons you taught me in the desert, Flynn?'

Her hands rested quietly on his chest now, neither holding him nor repulsing him. She needed to know the truth, and needed him to tell it to her. Gabrielle had implied that he felt something for her, but had she been right?

'Do you remember that night, Flynn?' she asked with a slight break in her voice. 'Recall what we shared then and the next day? Or has my memory been playing tricks?'

He stiffened beneath her touch then pushed her away and walked over to the window. He ran a hand around the back of his neck, kneading the tense muscles. 'I remember a lot of things, Natalie. I remember very clearly your telling me that you regretted it ever happening!'

'I remember that also, but what I want to know now is if I was right to accuse you of sleeping with me to get information about Marcus.' She clenched her hands into fists, inwardly preparing herself for the pain if it came. 'Tell me the truth, Flynn.'

A bitter kind of amusement crossed his face, making her heart ache. 'I really don't see where this is leading to. What's the point of opening old wounds, Natalie?' He shrugged, pushing his hands deep into his trouser pockets, his shoulders hunching slightly. 'What happened between us is in the past. Let's leave it there and get on with our lives. I'm sure Marcus would much prefer that. I know I would if I were in his position.'

'And what position is that, Flynn?'

His eyes glittered dangerously even though his face remained expressionless. 'Let's stop playing games, Natalie. I'm far too tired and far too busy to indulge in such childishness.' He walked away from the window, barely glancing at her as he headed for the door, but this time it was her turn to step in his way.

'I agree. The time for play-acting is over. It's time to tell the truth once and for all. I'll go first, shall I?' She watched him closely, seeing how his face closed up. It took all her courage to carry on, that plus a sense of desperation. All she would get was this one chance to make him understand how important it was that neither of them should lie for whatever reason!

'I am not in love with Marcus. I thought I was for a long time but I realised a while ago that I had been mistaken.'

He sighed heavily. 'Look, Natalie, your feelings, or lack of them, for Marcus Cole are none of my concern.'

It hurt to hear him say that in such an indifferent tone but she wouldn't give up, not yet, not until he had told her the truth, no matter what it was. 'Is that right? So you really don't care one way or the other, Flynn?'

Something flashed across his face. 'What do you want me to say, Natalie? You made it plain how you felt about me and the way I used you.'

He laid a deliberate emphasis on the last words and she winced. 'Yes. I was bitterly hurt. Finding out that you had deliberately become involved in my life so that you could find out about Marcus came as a shock. It knocked me sideways if you want the truth. But I want you to answer one question: did you sleep with me as a way to get that information?'

'There's really no point in this!'

'Then I can only take that to mean yes.' She turned away but not fast enough to hide the agony in her eyes from him.

'Natalie, I . . .' He reached out and caught her, turning her round to face him, then groaned deeply. 'No! How could you imagine that after what we shared?' His hands gentled on her. 'I wanted you for no other reason than making love to you was the single most important thing in the world right then. It had nothing to do with Marcus or what I was trying to find out. Nothing to do with anything but the aching need I had to hold you and make you mine!'

The sincerity in his voice couldn't be doubted. Natalie felt warmth run through her, erasing days upon days of numbing cold. She smiled up at him through glistening eyes, loving him at that moment more than ever. 'You don't know how I've prayed that that would be your answer, Flynn,' she whispered brokenly. 'I was so hurt when I overheard you and Doyle talking that I closed my mind to what you were trying to tell me. I was afraid that it would be more lies.'

'I've never deliberately lied to you, Natalie. Perhaps I wasn't totally honest about what I was trying to do but when it all began I had no idea of the implications.' He smiled thinly. 'It seems that even the best-laid plans can go wrong.'

'Perhaps not completely wrong.' She drew a quick little breath. 'You see, Flynn, I've fallen in love with you.'

The silence seemed to echo in the room then Flynn gave a harsh, incredulous laugh. 'What is this, Natalie? Another one of your little games? You seem to be full of them today!'

His tone stung but she faced him squarely. 'I've already told you I'm not playing games any more. I love you, Flynn.'

His eyes were glacial, burning with an icy flame which chilled her. 'You really expect me to believe that? That you've suddenly discovered that you don't love Marcus but me?'

'Yes, that's exactly what I want you to believe. But perhaps it is difficult to take it in.' She laughed huskily. 'I've had a while to get used to the idea, you see. Still, don't they say that sometimes actions speak much louder than any amount of words?'

Her heart was thundering, her whole body tense with fear. What if she had made a mistake and, despite what he had just said, Flynn felt nothing for her? He'd said that he had wanted her but... Before her courage deserted her completely she reached out and ran her hands up his chest to loop them around his neck while she drew his head down.

'In God's name, Natalie...!'

Her mouth drank in the heated words, the hard resistance of his lips mirrored by the tension in his body. Deliberately she moved closer and let her body brush lightly against his; she felt the way his hands came up to grip her waist and start to move her away from him but she refused to go. Her tongue traced the hard, unyielding outline of his mouth in a slow caress and she felt the shudder which ran through him with a flare of elation. Despite the impression he was trying to give he wasn't totally unmoved by the kiss!

Her fingers slid into the thick hair at his nape as she drew his head down further and deepened the kiss, her tongue pushing its way past the barrier of his hard lips to incite his to join it in a heady, sensual rhythm, yet still Flynn made no attempt to respond and the elation faded. Had she really misjudged the situation so badly? Didn't he care?

Tears slid down her cheeks and across their mouths and she heard Flynn utter a low exclamation which seemed to be torn from him. His hands lifted to cup her face while he kissed her back with a heat and urgency which ran in shock waves through her body. Now he was the instigator, his mouth making its urgent, hungry demands as he pushed her on and on towards a response which left her weak with longing so that she could only cling to him.

He drew back at last, eyes burning with a passion he made no attempt to hide as he trailed kisses over her eyelids, her cheeks, drying her tears with his ardour.

'I love you, Flynn,' she whispered urgently while she pressed frantic, imploring kisses along his jaw until he drew away with a harsh sigh.

'How do you know?'

'What do you mean?' She pulled back, confused by the question, and saw him smile with a bitter irony.

'You've already admitted that you thought you were in love with Marcus for a long time, so how can you be sure that's changed, that what you feel for me isn't just the result of this passion we arouse in one another?'

'No! I knew I was in love with you that first time, that night in the desert. I know how I feel, Flynn, and it's completely different from how I ever felt about Marcus!'

He set her away from him, turning his back on her as he walked over to the window again. Natalie wanted to run to him and make him believe her but when she took a step towards him he stopped her. 'No. That isn't the way, Natalie. Passion cannot be allowed to dictate this time!'

Her heart seemed to freeze. 'Meaning that's all you feel for me?'

He swung round, big and arrogant as he glared at her. 'Meaning that passion is a powerful emotion! It can be devastating suddenly to discover just how powerful. As you did when we made love, Natalie.'

Colour flooded her pale face but he was relentless as he came across to her and made her look at him. 'You were a virgin until that night. You'd had little or no experience.' He laughed harshly. 'I just wonder if the guilt you felt afterwards isn't still very much alive, and if convincing yourself that you're in love with me isn't a means of appeasing it?'

'No!' She tore herself away from him, eyes blazing with hurt. 'I don't feel at all guilty about loving you, O'Rourke! Oddly enough I never did. Oh, I might think I'm totally crazy, a complete fool, might feel a lot of things, but not guilty!'

'How can you be so sure? Have you seen Marcus since you got back?'

His tone was so reasonable; he might have been discussing anything, not the fact that she had just declared her love for him! Yet Natalie strove to match his mood, wondering if it would help convince him that she knew her own mind. 'No. I tried phoning his flat, to speak to you actually, but he wasn't there.'

'I finally tracked him down a few days ago.'

'And did you tell him what's been going on and that you've been investigating him?'

'Yes. Now that he's been eliminated as the main suspect, I needed his help to get to the bottom of things.'

'Oh, I'm sure he was pleased to hear that he'd been under suspicion!'

'Marcus is a realist. He understood only too well my reasons. He would have done the same thing himself if our positions had been reversed.'

'And did you tell him about us?'

'I told him that I had gone to Egypt with you and why, and what happened about you being kidnapped.' He shrugged. 'As for the rest, I left that up to you to tell him or not as you chose.'

He made it sound of such little consequence to him that Natalie's heart ached afresh. 'I see. Then maybe I should go to see Marcus myself?'

'That's up to you but perhaps it would help you get everything into perspective.'

'So that's your advice, is it, Flynn? Go and see Marcus and test out these feelings I have, see if they're real or merely a figment of my guilty conscience?'

His eyes glittered dangerously before he carefully blanked all expression from his face. 'That seems to be the sensible thing to do.'

He sounded almost indifferent to the outcome but Natalie had seen that betraying glint in his eyes that he hadn't been quick enough to hide and wasn't fooled. 'And what if I discover that it has nothing to do with imagination, that what I feel for you, Flynn, is real? What happens then?'

Every bone in his face seemed to contract yet when he stretched his hand out and touched her cheek with the very tips of his fingers it was the lightest, tenderest of caresses. 'Then, Natalie, you and I need to talk!'

As a declaration it barely rated a mention but it was enough to make hope surge to life inside her and flow sweetly through her veins. She smiled, letting him see everything she felt for him, and heard the soft indrawn breath he took with a feeling of triumph. Whatever impression Flynn had tried to give, this meant more to him than he was confessing!

'Where will you be? How can I contact you?' she asked quietly.

'Doyle will know. Just get a message through to him and he'll pass it on.' He let his hand drop and walked to the door, his knuckles showing white through the tanned skin as he gripped the handle. 'If I don't hear from you then I shall understand.'

It was the hardest thing in the world to let him walk out of the flat. Natalie's heart was breaking but she didn't attempt to call him back and make him stay. Flynn was determined that she shouldn't make a mistake so she would do as he wanted, but it didn't stop her from feeling scared. What if Flynn was simply trying to find a way out because what she'd told him had been something he hadn't wanted to hear? She closed her mind to that painful thought, clinging on to the memory of how he had touched her just now, so gently, so tenderly, to keep hope alive. She loved him and no matter what it took she was going to convince him of that most important fact!

Where was Marcus?

Natalie paced the floor, wondering where else she could try. Flynn had said that he'd spoken to him but so far she'd had no luck tracking him down. He seemed to have disappeared again and she was getting desperate as the days slipped past.

She had tried his sister, Becky, but she'd had no idea where he'd gone. Now that Becky was married Natalie didn't see so much of her and she wondered if it was that which had seemed to set a certain constraint on their conversation, most noticeably when she'd asked after Becky's husband, Rob. Several times over the past two years Natalie had wondered just how successful her friend's marriage was, but she had too many other things on her mind right now to dwell on it.

Suddenly overcome by a need to do something positive, she picked up her bag and in a very short time was ringing Marcus's doorbell. It would probably be a wasted journey, of course, but she had to... The sight of Marcus at the door left her speechless.

'Natalie? Is anything wrong? Here, come inside.'

He led her into the sitting-room, urging her into a chair as she continued to stare dumbly at him before finally finding her voice. 'Where have you been, Marcus?' she demanded hoarsely. 'I've been trying to get hold of you for days!'

He sat down, running a hand wearily over his face. He looked desperately tired, deep lines etched into his face, his dark grey eyes shadowed, and Natalie felt a pang of concern.

'Are you all right?'

'Yes. I'm sorry if you've been worried but there was something I had to attend to. It's been taking up most of my time recently. But what was so urgent that you've been trying to get hold of me?' He sat up, studying her intently. 'It hasn't anything to do with O'Rourke and that mess he got you into? I tore him off a strip when I found out that he'd involved you. He swore there would be no future repercussions but knowing the kind of people he's been dealing with one can't be certain!'

It had everything to do with Flynn, but not how Marcus imagined! Natalie glanced down, wondering what he would say if she told him the reason why she was here. Marcus had been an important part of her life for so long now, lending it the stability she'd needed so desperately from the time her parents had died. He had been her rock, always there to help when she'd needed it, and he would always be dear to her, but what she felt for him bore no resemblance to what she felt for Flynn!

'No, that's all been sorted out, hopefully, although I have to confess that I'm still not certain what's been going on.'

'I imagine O'Rourke deemed it safer not to tell you too much. It's been a bad business, Natalie, and from what he's told me it still isn't over. But if anyone can get to the bottom of it then O'Rourke can.' He sighed. 'I'm only sorry I wasn't around to give him the assistance he needed, although in the circumstances perhaps that wasn't what he wanted!' He added wryly, 'But I've been caught up with problems of my own. In fact I'll be going away again in a few days' time. If you need me for anything then leave a message with my office, Natalie. I'll make sure I get back to you as soon as I can.'

Natalie smiled. 'You mustn't worry about me, Marcus.'

He returned her smile, the strain easing from his face for a moment. 'I can't help it, Natalie. We've known each other a long time now and you're very dear to me.'

Tears stung her eyes at the admission and she leant forward and took his hand, holding it between both of hers. 'As you are to me,' she said softly. 'You've always

been there for me, Marcus, whenever I've needed
someone to lean on. Your friendship has meant a lot to
me and I want you to know that.'

He turned his hand over, capturing hers and holding
it while he stared quietly into her eyes. 'I'm glad, but
why do I get the feeling you're trying to tell me something, Natalie?' He laughed gently when her colour rose.
'I know you too well, don't I?'

She looked down at their linked hands then slowly
drew hers away. 'You do,' she said with a small laugh.
'There's no fooling you, is there?' She took a deep
breath. 'It's Flynn, you see.'

'O'Rourke? What do you mean? There isn't some sort
of problem he didn't tell me about, is there?' Marcus's
tone had hardened and Natalie hurried to allay his fears.

'No, not that kind, at least. And nothing we can't work
out,' she said softly, unaware of how much her voice
gave away.

Marcus smiled understandingly. 'I think I see now.
Are you in love with him, then, Natalie?'

'Yes,' she whispered.

'And how does he feel about you?'

Her face glowed with happiness. 'I think . . . *hope* that
Flynn feels the same way I do! So what advice would
you give me, Marcus?'

'Absolutely none. I don't imagine that you need any.'

He stood up and took her hands to draw her to her
feet. 'I always knew that it would happen one day, that
you'd find the man you'd fall in love with. Oh, I know
that you fancied I was that man but deep down I always
felt that one day you'd discover it wasn't so.' He laughed
as she flushed. 'Don't be embarrassed, Natalie, because
there's no need. I had even made up my mind that we
should talk about it, work through why you should feel

the way you did. I was just there at a time when you needed someone badly, and I'm only glad that I was able to fulfil that role in your life.'

'You did, Marcus. Thank you.' She smiled back at him, no longer embarrassed that he should have known all along about her feelings for him and grateful that he had never tried to play upon them. But there again, that was the kind of man he was.

'As for O'Rourke,' he continued, 'well, he isn't an easy person to get to know but I've learned enough over the years we've worked together to realise that he's one of the best. Just be happy, Natalie. That's all I've ever wanted for you.'

'Thank you.' The sincerity in his voice brought a lump to her throat. She reached up and kissed him lightly on the cheek then said goodbye and left, her heart swelling with joy. Marcus's blessing had put the seal on her happiness and now there were no uncertainties in her mind; there'd been none before she'd come, but Flynn had been right. She had needed to see Marcus and take that final step from the past into the future...

He was waiting for her when she arrived. Natalie had spent the flight in a state of nervous tension. What if he hadn't got her message or decided not to come? He had told her that he had wanted her but never once had Flynn actually said that he loved her!

By the time the plane landed Natalie had felt sick with nerves. She'd come through Customs and collected her luggage then suddenly looked up and there he was...

For a moment neither of them moved. Then Flynn held his hand out and Natalie went and slipped hers into it, loving the way his fingers tightened so possessively around hers.

Flynn tossed her bags into the back of the Jeep then climbed behind the wheel and gunned the engine, heading out of the city. Natalie rested her head back against the seat, letting the hot wind blow her hair into a tangle around her face as they drove on until the desert welcomed them on all sides. Only then did Flynn pull the vehicle off the road and cut the engine, leaving them alone in the whispering, expectant silence.

'Well, Natalie? Did you do as I suggested?' He stared straight ahead, face impassive, voice level. Only his hands, locked tightly around the wheel, betrayed any emotion.

Natalie reached across and laid her hand on his, love overwhelming her. Even now he was giving her room to change her mind. 'Yes. I saw Marcus.'

'And?'

'And...you were right.' She felt him flinch and laughed gently, drawing out the moment the better to savour it. 'Right to make me go and see him.' Her fingers linked through his as their lives would hopefully be linked. 'I have no doubts at all, Flynn. I love you—you and no one else.'

'Natalie, I...!' Words seemed to be suddenly beyond him as he turned and pulled her into his arms, kissing her with a hunger which he made no attempt to hide. When he drew back his aqua eyes were filled with an emotion which stole her breath and made her heart leap.

'I love you, Natalie. I love you more than I can possibly tell you. I shall love you until the day we die. I've never said that to any woman before because I've never felt this way. All I want now is to spend the rest of my life convincing you that it's true!'

'Oh, Flynn!' She kissed him with all the love she felt, a kiss which made promises and asked for commitment, a kiss which he returned just as urgently.

When he drew her round to nestle her head against his shoulder, she sighed. 'I've been so scared. Even coming here today I kept thinking, What if you weren't here, what if you really didn't care how I felt? It all happened so fast and so unexpectedly.'

'It did. We fell in love before we knew it, before we really knew one another, and that's something we must make up for.' He brushed her mouth with a disturbing kiss which made her ache, smiling when he met her eyes and read the message in their depths, the need she couldn't hide. 'I know. I feel it too, sweet. But we need to clear up all the misunderstandings so that they won't ever get between us in the future.'

'If you're sure?'

He must have felt her tension because he ran his hand down her arm in a tender caress. 'I am. We need to talk about it, Natalie.' He tilted her face up and stared quietly into her eyes. 'I am not nor ever have been involved in anything criminal.'

She gave a small smile. 'I'd already reached that conclusion.'

'Had you indeed? Based on what?' His eyebrows quirked.

'Oh, simply that the man I love couldn't possibly be involved in anything like that...despite all the indications to the contrary!'

He laughed deeply. 'And there have been an awful lot of those, haven't there? If I had set out to make you suspicious then I couldn't have done a better job!'

'And speaking of *jobs*, just what do you do?' Natalie drew back and stared solemnly at him. 'I somehow don't think it's insurance!'

'But that's where you're wrong.' He ran a fingertip across her mouth, smiling with a very masculine triumph when she took a shuddery little breath which told him exactly what he was doing to her. 'You really do have the most deliciously sensitive lips, Natalie... Where was I? Ah, yes—my job. I own a firm which organises protection for a variety of people who are at risk, from pop stars who need bodyguards to heads of state who might be the target of terrorist attacks. It is insurance—*life* insurance of a very special kind!'

'It sounds terribly dangerous.' Her voice reflected her sudden fear and he hastened to reassure her.

'Anything can be dangerous if it isn't thought through properly. I aim to minimise any risks by planning. What happened in Cairo to you was unprecedented.'

'Can you tell me what it was all about, and how Marcus came to be involved to the extent that you thought he might be working against you?'

Flynn sighed, leaning back in the seat and drawing her more comfortably against him as though he enjoyed holding her. 'It still isn't completely cleared up. There are questions which need answering, not least of which is exactly who was behind the leak of information.'

'But you're sure it wasn't Marcus?'

He smiled tightly. 'Oh, yes. Marcus was the number one suspect because the job I was working on was set up initially through him. He had a client who needed extra-special protection and contacted me to arrange it. The client, an Italian by the name of Alessi, was the only witness in a massive fraud trial which has recently gone to court in Rome. His testament was crucial if there were to be any convictions but several highly influential people were determined that he would never give that testimony.'

'How dreadful!' Natalie made no attempt to disguise her horror, and felt Flynn's arms tighten around her.

'That's why I was so desperate to find out the information I needed, Natalie. There had been an attempt made on Alessi's life once when they discovered where he was being hidden. I couldn't afford to allow a second one to go ahead.

'Originally, Alessi fled to England fearing for his safety. He hired Marcus when extradition papers were served to make him go back to Rome for the trial. In the end he only agreed to go when my firm was hired to protect him. Only two of us knew where he was being hidden—myself and Marcus—so it seemed a natural assumption that if the leak hadn't come from me it must have come from him.'

'And that's when you decided to see what you could find out about Marcus...from me?'

'Yes. It seemed to make sense. I had to tread carefully, as you'll appreciate, but I had to get to the bottom of it as quickly as I could. One part of me said, No, Marcus Cole wouldn't be involved, but...' He shrugged. 'A lot of money changed hands for that information, Natalie. And that can make people do things that they wouldn't consider normally.'

'So you planned on using me right from the moment you heard my message on the phone?' She couldn't quite keep the hurt from her voice and heard him sigh.

'I wish I could deny it, honey, but it would be a lie, and one thing I shall never do is lie to you. Hearing you seemed like a God-given opportunity. I wanted to find out about the people Marcus knew, his associates, friends, anything which would link him to the leak.' He sighed. 'I'm not proud of what I planned but I had little choice. There was only a matter of weeks left before the trial and the people involved were getting desperate.'

'I understand.'

'Do you?' He tilted her face to look deep into her eyes. 'I never intended that you be put at risk. The thought that those people were following me never crossed my mind until you were kidnapped!'

'I'm not sure I understand.' She frowned. 'What do you mean they were following you?'

He ran a finger lightly over the wrinkles on her brow, smoothing them out. 'Exactly that. The people involved had found out where Alessi was by following *me*. Someone had tipped them off that I was organising his protection.'

'But if it wasn't Marcus then who told them?'

'I don't know yet but I have a man working on it. The leak has come from Marcus's end, I'm sure of that, but not sure who was behind it. But I shall find out, you can believe me!'

Natalie didn't need to question that. Whatever Flynn had to do he would do it. It was part of his integrity to put his heart and soul into a job. Could she really hold his using her against him, now that she knew the kind of stakes he'd been playing for?

Perhaps he understood where her thoughts were with that perception he had exhibited so many times in the past. He drew her round to face him, holding her lightly by the shoulders, his eyes intent and filled with sincerity. 'I did what I had to do, Natalie. The fact that it soon started to conflict with my personal feelings was something I had to put to one side. A man's life was at stake.'

She smiled, running her hand lightly down his cheek, loving the fact that she had the right to do so. 'I understand, Flynn. Honestly I do.'

He kissed her quickly with a depth of emotion which left her breathless. 'Thank heavens for that! I knew I was starting to feel far more than I should for you in the circumstances, but I couldn't explain what was going on!'

'Because you didn't trust me? You...you thought that I might be involved through Marcus?' she asked hollowly, hurt clouding her eyes.

'Not once I'd got to know you!' His hands tightened, forcing her to look at him and believe what he was telling her. 'Oh, perhaps in the beginning I did wonder, but I soon realised that any involvement you might have had would have been purely accidental, a chance meeting with a contact Marcus had. All I wanted from you was an insight into who he knew and how he had been acting recently.'

'And the fact that he had been acting oddly didn't help.' She sighed. 'He told me that he's been busy with something or other but didn't go into any detail, although I had the feeling that he was worried about it.'

'I got that impression too but he told me no more than he told you. Marcus plays his hand close to his chest.'

Natalie laughed. 'If there ever was a case of the pot calling the kettle... No one could play his cards closer than you, O'Rourke!'

He grinned disarmingly, eyes glittering as they skimmed her face. 'I'm not doing it now, though, am I, sweet? I'm sure you have a pretty clear idea what's on my mind at present!'

She couldn't stop the blush which spread up her cheeks and looked away when he laughed softly, so seductively that the heat flowed through every bit of her. She took a sharp little breath, striving for calm. 'So what happens now to this man, Alessi?'

Flynn sobered. 'He's given his testimony and I've just finalised the details to have him and his family moved to someplace where no one will ever find them.' He shrugged. 'It won't be easy for him, making a new life in a strange country, but at least he'll be safe and know that his family won't be at risk.'

'I suppose that's some comfort. But did his testimony really help?'

'Yes, it did. The trial is being summed up today and everyone seems confident that those involved in the fraud will go down for a long time.'

'I'm glad. He's been very brave, testifying like that, knowing the risks.' She shivered suddenly. 'I was only in that man's custody for a day but I was scared!'

Flynn swore roughly, pulling her to him to hold her tightly. 'I shall never forgive myself for that, Natalie!' He drew away. 'It's made me realise that I could never put you at risk again. You're far too precious to me. So I've decided to take more of a back seat than I have done up to now, run the firm and set up the operations without getting personally involved.' He shrugged. 'I've built up a team of good men over the past few years, men I can rely on, so I shall start delegating. It'll be no bad thing because the business has been expanding rapidly and it needs me to spend more time on developing its future than I have done.'

'Are you sure, Flynn? Sure that you won't miss a more active involvement?'

'Absolutely. I've got tired of living out of a suitcase recently. And the risks involved have definitely lost their appeal when I weigh them up against other factors.'

'Such as?' she asked softly.

'Such as living with you, making a life for us together. That will give me all the thrills I need.'

'I love you so much, Flynn,' she said, with her heart in her eyes.

'And you're quite sure that you're over Marcus?' He made no attempt to disguise his need for reassurance and Natalie smiled.

'Yes. Marcus will always be a very dear friend because he's been a part of my life for so long and was there when I needed him most after my parents died. I was at a low point then; I'd been sent to live with an elderly aunt of my father's who I didn't even know and although she was kind enough she never showed me much affection.'

'It must have been hard for you.'

Natalie shrugged. 'It wasn't that bad because Marcus helped me to adjust by being there and filling all the missing roles: counsellor, protector, adviser. He was and always will be a very dear friend but what I feel for him bears no resemblance to what I feel for you, Flynn!'

'As long as you're sure it isn't guilt over our sleeping together?'

'Oh, I feel a lot of things about that . . . but not guilt!'

He understood what she meant only too well, his face darkening with desire as he drew her to him and kissed her hungrily. He drew back and smiled with purely masculine satisfaction at her immediate response. 'So, Natalie, how long do we have before the world intrudes?'

Natalie snuggled into his arms. 'Not nearly as long as I would like. I have to be back in London in forty-eight hours to complete the final details on the Egypt account, and that's going to be an intrusion in itself!'

'Why do you say that?' He frowned.

'Oh, only because once the women get to see those pictures of you, Flynn O'Rourke, I shall be fighting them off by the cartload. They're almost alarmingly good and the promotion promises to break all records from the response we've had so far!'

He laughed softly. 'I shall only ever have eyes for you, Natalie, but maybe you should stake your claim right away, although I wonder how poor old Renshaw will take the news that we're getting married?'

'Probably with as much surprise as me!' She eased back and glared at him. 'Was that supposed to be a proposal? If so it was a miserable effort!'

He laughed deeply, running a finger lazily down her cheek while he watched the flames dance to life in her dark eyes. 'I'm afraid I haven't had a lot of practice, sweet. But maybe I can make a better job of it.' He let her go and started the engine, turning the Jeep back towards the city.

'Am I allowed to ask where we're going?' Natalie said haughtily.

'Not worried I'm kidnapping you, are you?' he teased. 'I've booked the suite again at the hotel, although hopefully this time I won't have to bribe the desk clerk so that he'll tell you there are no other rooms available.'

'Flynn O'Rourke, you are a conniving wretch!'

'But you love me,' he said confidently, leaning over to kiss her quickly before turning back as the Jeep veered alarmingly. 'But to continue, we'll go back to the hotel, get changed and have dinner. Then...' He paused meaningfully and Natalie felt her heart start racing wildly.

'Then?' she queried breathlessly.

He looked at her, love filling his aqua eyes. 'Then I shall drive you somewhere quiet on the edge of the desert and claim that kiss you still owe me and ask you again. What do you think your answer will be, Natalie?'

Natalie closed her eyes, picturing the scene: the desert lying still and beautiful under the midnight sky with the moon a silver crescent overhead, and her in Flynn's arms while he asked her to share his life.

'Yes,' she whispered, then repeated it in a joyous shout. 'Yes!'

New from Harlequin Romance a very special six-book series by

The town of Hard Luck, Alaska, needs women!

The O'Halloran brothers, who run a bush-plane service called **Midnight Sons**, are heading a campaign to attract women to Hard Luck. *(Location: north of the Arctic Circle. Population: 150—mostly men!)*

"Debbie Macomber's *Midnight Sons* series is a delightful romantic saga. And each book is a powerful, engaging story in its own right. Unforgettable!"

—Linda Lael Miller

TITLE IN THE MIDNIGHT SONS SERIES:

UNLOCK THE DOOR TO GREAT ROMANCE
AT BRIDE'S BAY RESORT

Join Harlequin's new across-the-lines series, set in an exclusive hotel on an island off the coast of South Carolina.

Seven of your favorite authors will bring you exciting stories about fascinating heroes and heroines discovering love at Bride's Bay Resort.

Look for these fabulous stories coming to a store near you beginning in January 1996.

Harlequin American Romance #613 in January
Matchmaking Baby by Cathy Gillen Thacker

Harlequin Presents #1794 in February
Indiscretions by Robyn Donald

Harlequin Intrigue #362 in March
Love and Lies by Dawn Stewardson

Harlequin Romance #3404 in April
Make Believe Engagement by Day Leclaire

Harlequin Temptation #588 in May
Stranger in the Night by Roseanne Williams

Harlequin Superromance #695 in June
Married to a Stranger by Connie Bennett

Harlequin Historicals #324 in July
Dulcie's Gift by Ruth Langan

Visit Bride's Bay Resort each month wherever Harlequin books are sold.

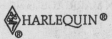 HARLEQUIN ®

BBAYG

Harlequin Romance ®

brings you

How the West was Wooed!

We've rounded up twelve of our most popular authors, and the result is a whole year of romance, Western style. Every month we'll be bringing you a spirited, independent woman whose heart is about to be lassoed by a rugged, handsome, one-hundred-percent cowboy! Watch for...

- March: **CLANTON'S WOMAN**—Patricia Knoll

- April: **A DANGEROUS MAGIC**—Patricia Wilson

- May: **THE BADLANDS BRIDE**—Rebecca Winters

- June: **RUNAWAY WEDDING**—Ruth Jean Dale

- July: **A RANCH, A RING AND EVERYTHING**—Val Daniels

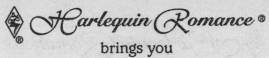

brings you

Some men are worth waiting for!

They're handsome, they're charming but, best of all, they're single! Twelve lucky women are about to discover that finding Mr. Right is not a problem—it's holding on to him.

In March the series continues with

#3401 THE ONLY MAN FOR MAGGIE
by Leigh Michaels

Karr Elliot wanted Maggie off his property but not out of his life. But Maggie didn't want a man—she wanted her own apartment!

Hold out for Harlequin Romance's heroes in coming months...

- April: THE RIGHT KIND OF MAN—Jessica Hart

- May: MOVING IN WITH ADAM—Jeanne Allan

- June: THE PARENT TRAP—Leigh Michaels

HOFH-3

Yo amo novelas con corazón!

Starting this March, Harlequin opens up to a whole new world of readers with two new romance lines in SPANISH!

Harlequin Deseo
- passionate, sensual and exciting stories

Harlequin Bianca
- romances that are fun, fresh and very contemporary

With four titles a month, each line will offer the same wonderfully romantic stories that you've come to love—now available in Spanish.

Look for them at selected retail outlets.

HARLEQUIN PRESENTS®

Harlequin brings you the best books, by the best authors!

ANNE MATHER

"...her own special brand of enchantment."
—Affaire de Coeur

&

LINDSAY ARMSTRONG

"...commands the reader's attention."
—Romantic Times

Next month:

***A WOMAN OF PASSION* by Anne Mather**
Harlequin Presents #1797

Ice maiden...or sensuous seductress? Only Matthew Aitken
guessed that Helen's cool exterior hid her passionate
nature...*but* wasn't he already involved with Fleur—who just
happened to be Helen's mother!

***TRIAL BY MARRIAGE* by Lindsay Armstrong**
Harlequin Presents #1798

To outsiders Sarah seemed like a typical
spinster schoolteacher.

Cliff Wyatt was the local hunk and could have his pick from a
harem of willing women. So why was he so interested in Sarah?

Harlequin Presents—the best has just gotten better!
Available in March wherever Harlequin books are sold.